THE HISTORY OF THE
SOMERSET COALFIELD

THE HISTORY OF THE SOMERSET COALFIELD

C G Down &
A J Warrington

RADSTOCK
MUSEUM

Copyright © 1971 & 2005 C G Down & A J Warrington

First published in 1971 by
David & Charles (Publishers) Ltd

This edition published in 2005 by
Radstock Museum
Waterloo Road
Radstock
BA3 3EP
www.radstockmuseum.co.uk

ISBN-10: 0-9551684-0-6
ISBN-13: 978-0-9551684-0-6

British Library Cataloguing in Publication Data
A catalogue record for this book is available from
the British Library

Cover design by Ben Green
Printed and bound in Great Britain by
Butler & Tanner Ltd, Frome and London

FOREWORD

It is nearly sixty years since the Somerset Coalfield entered the final chapter of its long history and joined, in 1947, the other sixteen British coalfields in the State Nationalisation of the Industry. However, twenty six years later market forces had brought about the demise of the last Somerset pit and the coalfield became the first in Britain to suffer the fate of total closure. Kilmersdon and Writhlington collieries were still operational when this book was originally published but in September 1973 the final tub of coal was raised and this marked the end of 2000 years of coalmining in Somerset.

Hence it was of lasting benefit that Down and Warrington visited the coalfield in its final years to observe its operations and obtain first hand knowledge and reports from its dedicated workforce. This book, the result of their investigations, remains to this day the most detailed account of an industry that once dominated social and economic life in the locality.

Twenty years ago and a decade after the last winding gear had been dismantled, the final shaft filled and capped and the pit-top sites smoothed over to accept the trade and industry of the 21st Century, the Radstock Museum was born. Located in the old Market Hall the Museum is situated alongside the former route of the Somersetshire Coal Canal, the Somerset and Dorset Railway and within close proximity of both Ludlows and Middle Pit colliery surfaces. The cover photograph, circa 1930, shows Ludlows Colliery and in the background one can see the Market Hall and the headgear of Middle Pit.

Visitors to the Museum have been fascinated with the archival documentation of this remarkable coalfield. This interest was further developed when the Museum undertook the European

Culture 2000 Project in 2004/05 resulting in a growing request for more detailed information about the coalfield.

In celebration of its twentieth anniversary, Radstock Museum is pleased to commission a reprint of Down and Warrington's "The History of the Somerset Coalfield" and thus ensuring this authoritative book will continue to provide a valuable source of information to present and future generations.

Ian McInnes
Nigel Carter
RADSTOCK MUSEUM 2005

LIST OF SUBSCRIBERS AND DEDICATIONS : 2005 EDITION

David J Barge
Mrs J Berry
Stephen Bletso
Dr Margaret Bowles in memory of Dr Frances Ashworth
Mrs E Browning in memory of Thomas Sims
Irene A Burchell
Mrs B Cameron
Roger and June Carter
Dennis Chedgy in memory of Frank Chedgy
Gary Chedgy
Dr R J Charles Chillcott
Stephen Cleaves in memory of my Grandfather, Howard Arthur Newth
Iain Dainty
Jack Denning in memory of Walter and Gladys Denning
Robyn Susan Dexter
Carolyn Drouin
Jack Edwards in memory of my dear Father, Bert
Clive Ellam
Richard Ellam
Sandra Fergusson in memory of Jack and Alice Fairhurst
Mr J Fussell in memory of Thomas Alfred Coombs
Mr G T G Garsed
George W Greene
Richard Gregory in memory of Ernest Jones
Maryce Grubb in memory of all local miners
Steve Grudgings in memory of Laura Ragg
Captain James Roy Hancock MBE RM and Mrs Sandra Frances Hancock
Mrs Frances Hardman
Michael Hawkins in memory of Charles and Annie Strawbridge
Sadie and Philip Haynes

Dennis Herbert

John Hitchens in memory of Clifford L Hitchens

Tony Howe in memory of my Grandfather, Albert Shearn (a Somerset miner)

Mr R K Jones

Mr J Kingman in memory of Arthur John Kingman and Lewis William Kingman

Richard Maggs

Mrs Betty Maidment in memory of my Father, Ernest Paradise

Clem and Maureen Maidment

Anne Miall

Ms B Milsom in memory of Mr W Milsom (Bud)

Mrs C Oatley for Mr Wilfred R F Smart

Richard Henry Offer

Roger Pike in memory of my Father, Herbie Pike

Christopher Powell

Darren Powell

Derek Powell

James Powell

Marian Prior in memory of my Grandfather, Robert Forester Bennett

Barry John Pritchard

Tom Randall

Spencer Ruddick

Dennis Sage

Martyn Sage

Peter Simpson

Martin Smith

John D Spratley

Mrs Dorothy Stevens in memory of Cyril James Stevens

J R Tanner

Bob Taylor in memory of Tom Taylor

Janice Taylor in memory of W C Wells

Mark Tredwen

Jeremy Veale

Wendy Walker

Tony Whitchurch

Mark Winfield in memory of George Henry Maggs

J R Young in memory of Charlie Young

Colin, Martin, June and Sue in memory of our Grandfather, Albert Maidment

Doris, Flo and Mervyn in memory of Albert Thomas Fowler (Bert)

Robert and Marjorie in memory of George Morris

To Betty from Doll

To Stuart from Gay

To Dad with love from Holly, Luke and Beth

In memory of Corbett, George, Fred and Ted Hearse (winding engine men)

CONTENTS

LIST OF ILLUSTRATIONS

TEXT ILLUSTRATIONS

We are grateful to the following for permission to use their
photographs: Bristol City Museum & Art Gallery (p104, below); B. Chapman (p138, below); the late S. Cook (p51); A. H.
Gore (p34); E. Jones (p137, above); H. T. Vranch (pp103; 189,
below; 190, above; 207). Other photographs are by the authors,
or from their collections.

PREFACE

This book had its origin in 1967 when a chance introduction brought together the authors' investigations. One of us had been working on the collieries, the other on transportation in the coalfield. Co-operation seemed desirable, and this book is the result.

We have investigated all the sites—by verbal enquiry, searching the written records, and examination on the spot. In connection with the latter we may mention our excavations on tramroad routes. These were assisted by a mine detector, which gave us worthwhile results, and the local villagers an amusing and interesting spectacle!

We have endeavoured to provide the reader with both an interesting and informative story, and a means of interpreting the scattered remains of Somerset coalmining that he may find. We have accumulated far more information than can be encompassed in a commercial publication and we have, therefore, tried to emphasise some of the interesting and lesser known aspects of the coalfield.

Finally, it is to be hoped that this work will, in some measure, be taken as a tribute to the colliers of Somerset; as a memorial—however brief—of their lives and activities, recorded before it is too late.

C. G. DOWN

A. J. WARRINGTON

Claremont
Eridge Road
Garndiffaith
Pontypool
Torfaen, NP4 7LU

KEY TO SYMBOLS USED ON ALL MAPS

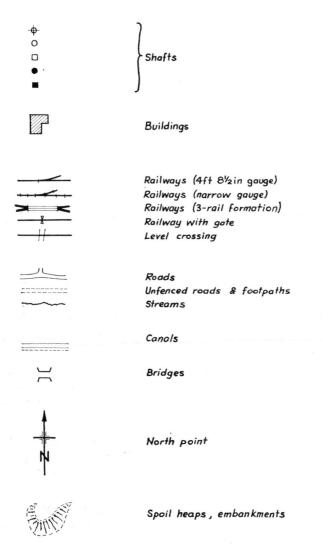

Shafts

Buildings

Railways (4ft 8½in gauge)
Railways (narrow gauge)
Railways (3-rail formation)
Railway with gate
Level crossing

Roads
Unfenced roads & footpaths
Streams

Canals

Bridges

North point

Spoil heaps, embankments

1 THE HISTORY IN OUTLINE

The Somerset coalfield occupies a position of peculiar ambivalence among the coalmining areas of the United Kingdom. It has always been regarded as a fascinating geological site; William 'Strata' Smith, the so-called 'Father of English Geology', who set down on paper the first discussion of stratigraphy, gained his information by investigating at Mearns Colliery. There are other famous names: George Greenwell and James McMurtrie, both of the Radstock Collieries, and both prolific writers; geologists such as Buckland, Conybeare and Staples; and Mr Stutchbury, surveyor to the Radstock Collieries, who was among the first to recognise the importance of good mining plans and who was chosen by the Government to assist in deliberations following the Haswell Colliery explosion, Co Durham, in 1844.[1]

Again, the coalfield achieved fame—or notoriety—from the geological conditions under which its miners laboured. It was well said that 'those who could successfully overcome these difficulties were capable of working coal in any part of the globe'.[2]

Three underground explosions, in 1893, 1895 and 1908, were amongst the first attributable solely to airborne coal dust and the recognition of this fact, as demonstrated in Somerset, contributed to colliery safety throughout the country.

Against this the coalfield was paradoxically unnoticed from the point of view of commercial production. It was a small coalfield in what remained a rural area, lacking the associated heavy industry that could have brought it fame and spoiled the countryside. Despite its proximity, Bristol, for centuries a

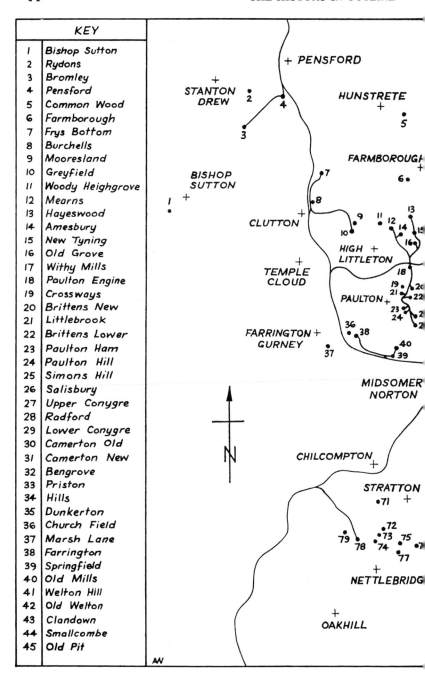

KEY	
1	Bishop Sutton
2	Rydons
3	Bromley
4	Pensford
5	Common Wood
6	Farmborough
7	Frys Bottom
8	Burchells
9	Mooresland
10	Greyfield
11	Woody Heighgrove
12	Mearns
13	Hayeswood
14	Amesbury
15	New Tyning
16	Old Grove
17	Withy Mills
18	Paulton Engine
19	Crossways
20	Brittens New
21	Littlebrook
22	Brittens Lower
23	Paulton Ham
24	Paulton Hill
25	Simons Hill
26	Salisbury
27	Upper Conygre
28	Radford
29	Lower Conygre
30	Camerton Old
31	Camerton New
32	Bengrove
33	Priston
34	Hills
35	Dunkerton
36	Church Field
37	Marsh Lane
38	Farrington
39	Springfield
40	Old Mills
41	Welton Hill
42	Old Welton
43	Clandown
44	Smallcombe
45	Old Pit

SOMERSET COALFIELD
GENERAL MAP

+MARKSBURY

PRISTON
+

TUNLEY
33 • +

27 TIMSBURY 32 34
+
29
30 31
35

28
CAMERTON + PEASEDOWN

RADSTOCK
44 50
43 45 49
41 48 51
46 +
53
42 47 54 52
57
58 55
59 56

KILMERSDON+

•69

•66
•67
HOLCOMBE 65 64 •60
+
+HIGHBURY •61
•70 68 + 62
COLEFORD 63 MELLS +

0   1   2

SCALE OF MILES

11.70

KEY	
46	Middle Pit
47	Ludlows
48	Tyning
49	Woodborough
50	Braysdown
51	Shoscombe
52	Foxcote
53	Lower Writhlington
54	Upper Writhlington
55	Huish
56	Kilmersdon
57	Wellsway
58	Norton Hill New
59	Norton Hill Old
60	Mells
61	Bilboa
62	Vobster
63	Breach
64	Newbury
65	Mackintosh
66	Luckington
67	Old Newbury
68	Coal Barton
69	Charmborough
70	Edford
71	New Rock
72	Old Rock
73	Strap
74	Sweetleaze
75	Nettlebridge
76	Barlake
77	Pitcot
78	Moorewood New
79	Moorewood Old

city of national renown, did not receive any financial benefit from Somerset coal.

For many centuries the coalfield was comparable with most others in its technical development but, with the age of steam and the mechanisation of mining, it began to lag behind. The capital needed for such developments had to be found by the coal and land owners within the coalfield; there was little outside help. And so the pits remained small and the coalfield became a backwater where men scratched a living in conditions that would have been the despair of miners from other areas.

UP TO 1790

Coalmining in Somerset has a very long ancestry. There is no reason to suppose that coal was used as a fuel in pre-Roman times and indeed the Romans themselves appear to have left coal outcrops largely undisturbed. Only one Roman writer appears to refer to coal, and, if so, this is where the history of Somerset coalmining begins. The writer Solinus (probably writing in the third century of the Christian era) makes a passing reference to a fuel used in the Temple of Minerva, presumed to be at Bath, to maintain the perpetual fires in the shrine. This fuel, instead of burning away to a white ash, as wood does, burnt to leave a stony residue. This is usually construed as meaning that coal was used.[3] The Fosseway, a Roman road from Bath, passed through the coalfield at its most accessible area—Stratton on the Fosse—so that coal would have been easy to obtain and transport once its value was recognised.

There are few contemporary references other than this until the 1400s, so coal was probably worked sporadically after Roman times but, with plenty of wood, the use of a fuel which required specialised techniques to extract it from the ground was largely unnecessary.

For several centuries Somerset mining continued in a small way; but it was not until the mid-1600s that an upsurge in activity occurred. Many details of the mines are known from legal actions resulting from this proliferation.[4] All parishes in which coal outcropped were explored and worked to some extent, Stratton, Farrington Gurney and High Littleton being the most important areas. Pits were named after a variety of conspicuous features, and strange names they were, too! — Bullock's Hill; Atkin's Gout; Ruth's Arse; Ringing Bell; Woody Heighgrove. The output from Somerset has been estimated as 10,000 tons annually in the mid-1500s; but by the late 1600s the figure had increased tenfold.[5] Demand came from a circle 20 miles around the coalfield as it was then known and transport could often be a three-day affair; but the large towns—Glastonbury, Shepton Mallet, Bath and Wells—and the many villages were all supplied with Somerset coal.

As the eighteenth century advanced, men became more adventurous and prospected in hitherto neglected areas. One adventurer, who must have accepted more risks than most, found coal in 1763 when Old Pit was sunk in Earl Waldegrave's Manor of Radstock. The story of this book really begins here, with this sinking that was to have such far-reaching effects. It is not proposed to deal at any length with the history of the coalfield before this, except when pits have spanned the period, and we would refer the reader to the excellent accounts published by Bulley in 1952-3, which cover the history of most aspects of the coalfield up to 1830.

1790 TO 1900

As the eighteenth century drew to a close, Somerset mining began the long climb to the peak of its achievement, reached in the first decades of the twentieth century. Increasingly, deep mines were being sunk in areas of the concealed coalfield and steam power for all purposes was rapidly being applied. All the technical improvements were made by outside engineers and borrowed from other coalfields.

The next problem was transporting the coal to the waiting markets. The Somersetshire Coal Canal was the first move in this direction. It was planned for commencement in 1795 with two branches, to Paulton and Radstock, but the latter branch was not really functional until 1815 when it had been converted into a tramroad.[6] This canal played an important part

B

in the development of the northern part of the coalfield; the
second canal scheme, the Dorset & Somerset Canal which obtained its Act in 1795, could have done the same for the southern area but it failed before completion and it is unlikely that
a significant amount of coal was ever carried by it.

It was the lack of main-line railways and the delay in their
eventual arrival that really frustrated the local coalowners. In
1861, Greenwell commented: 'The great bulk of this coalfield is dormant . . . for the want of railway accommodation . . .', and he and McMurtrie wrote that the Bristol &
North Somerset Railway, at its present rate of progress, 'may
be completed some time during the next century'. A report of
November 1872[7] said, 'The railways projected and in course
of construction will afford considerable facilities for opening
collieries'. Railways were not an unmixed blessing, however,
for they allowed coal into Somerset from other coalfields.
Anstie thought that, if competition came, 'it is doubtful if the
coals . . . would pay for working . . .

The first railway to serve the coalfield was the Wilts Somer-
set & Weymouth Railway, which was opened from Frome to
Radstock as a broad gauge mineral line in 1854. From this
line, the Westbury Iron Co constructed a branch to serve their
Newbury Colliery. No other railway arrived until the 1870s,
the B & NSR being opened in 1873 and the Somerset & Dorset
Railway extension to Bath in 1874. Both the B & NSR and the
WSWR became part of the Great Western Railway and
formed a through standard gauge route from Bristol to Frome.
The S & D formed a through route from Bath to Bournemouth. The final construction was by the GWR, which built
a branch from Hallatrow to Camerton in 1882 and extended
it to Limpley Stoke in 1910. This railway used the general
course of the SCC's Paulton branch, while the earlier S & D
utilised the route of the SCC's Radstock tramroad. The canal
was virtually disused by the 1890s. There were many other
abortive railway schemes: the joint promotion by the London
& South Western Railway and the GWR in 1862; the Nettlebridge Valley Railway of 1874; the Priston and Blagdon light
railway schemes of the 1900s; and the Radstock Wrington &

Congresbury Junction Railway, a ridiculous idea of the 1880s.

The construction of railways extended the market for coal, though these extensions were limited and usually unsuccessful. In the 1880s Edford Colliery, 4 miles from the nearest railway, was sending foundry coke to London where, despite competition from the best products of Durham and South Wales, 'it maintains its supremacy'.[8] Earlier, in 1844, the Timsbury and Greyfield proprietors had established coal wharves at Swindon, Oxford, Twyford and Slough GWR stations for the sale of their product.[9] Generally, however, only local markets were supplied, Bath consumers being the most important. Bristol was not considered as a market, though only a dozen miles away, except by the Timsbury and Radstock collieries, which both established short-lived coal wharves in that city.

The reasons for this limitation of sale are hard to find. In all probability the collieries had built up local markets over the years which suited their production capacities and provided a reliable sale for their coals. Although most collieries tried coke ovens, only those at the Mendip pits had even a small success. There was, in short, no need to look further afield than local markets, nor the capital to develop the pits to supply them. In 1861 it was said that the coalfield was capable of producing at least five times its current output of 750,000 tons per year if worked to its full extent.[10] Unfortunately, the coalfield was not so worked; the canal and railways provided boosts to production and incentives to modernise but the impetus was not lasting.

Not that there were no attempts to remedy this state of affairs. Mr W. Morgans was a vigorous campaigner who published his views on the potential value of the coalfield to the Bristol City Docks. Talking generally he says, 'it would hardly be expected that . . . the mining industry could lag so far behind that of other coalfields', and, in particular, slates the coalowners for sinking their pits in ill-advised sites, for the poor quality of their management, and for not providing enough capital to expand the industry. His main thesis was that the city docks should use local coal for bunkering rather than import coal from South Wales. In 1888, for example, the docks shipped 14 tons of coal on coastal vessels and 4,570 tons for export; but 245,267 tons were imported from South Wales and elsewhere.

Another point Morgans made concerned railway freight charges. The GWR, he said, charged 2s 3d per ton to carry coal from Radstock to Trowbridge, a distance of 18 miles. But it only cost 5s 8d to bring coal from Cannock to Trowbridge (via the London & North Western Railway), a distance of 136 miles. It cost no less than 4s 11d to take Somerset coal to Reading GWR station. Even the railways themselves were criticised as having been constructed with 'less regard for gradient than might have been expected when serving a coalfield'.

Morgans was, unfortunately, very much a prophet in the wilderness but the railways do provide some interesting information. The following figures show the amount of coal consigned over the GWR and the S & D from pits in Somerset: [11]

Year	via GWR (tons)	via S & D (tons)	Total coalfield output (tons)
1888	303,639	45,475	983,078
1889	250,740	40,371	876,254
1890	286,840	32,081	921,870
1891	296,325	30,341	915,170
1892	307,296	42,749	855,690
1893	201,404	24,528	575,469★
1894	?	?	835,926
1895	308,371	44,222	841,491
1896	318,427	43,851	871,373
1897	345,719	50,872	860,002
1898	386,799	57,283	990,787
1899	426,639	47,916	983,973

★Low output due to a strike

The first point arising is that only a third of the total coalfield output was carried by rail, even after railway construction was virtually completed. The canal would at this period have affected the figures very little, and so it must be concluded that nearly two-thirds of the coalfield output was disposed of locally by road. Secondly, the GWR carried about eight times as much coal as the S & D. If we list the total number of pits connected to each system in, for example, 1899, then twelve were on the GWR and two on the S & D. The six pits at Radstock and Writhlington had connections to both systems and must have made greater use of the GWR, so the construction of the S & D benefited the coalfield little. Even after 1899 the GWR gained two new large collieries to the S & D's one, so these proportions doubtless remained similar.

At the beginning of the 1800s there were some sixty major collieries in Somerset, plus perhaps thirty smaller ones. In 1868 there were sixty-four pits at work, but by 1894 only twenty-seven, of which about five had been sunk since 1850 and three had been deepened and modernised. Which pits had been lost?

The passing of the 1800s saw the complete eclipse of mining in the Paulton area, where each hillside had once had a colliery. Most of the accessible coal had been exhausted and the closure of one pit meant a greater burden of water for another. The area was served only by the SCC, the GWR coming too late to save these pits from closure. Of the many Timsbury collieries, only the two Conygre pits were still at work, while further east the Jarretts' Camerton Collieries flourished. Still further eastwards the coal was under deep cover. Significant development was yet to come.

Around Radstock two of the Waldegrave pits had gone, including the pioneer Old Pit, closed after nearly a century of mining life. The two Welton pits, once of some importance, were also shut. Generally, however, the pits were in good shape, newly deepened to the Farrington Series and with a bright future ahead. In the Mendips, lacking every form of transport other than roads, the pits had withered and often died. Strap Colliery the biggest development of the century, had closed after a life of ten years, killed by the isolation. However, total annual output for Somerset was nearly at the million ton mark; demand was still on the increase and mines were, for the while, poised to exploit it.

1900 TO 1947

The new century brought Somerset annual output to its highest level ever—1,250,000 tons in the first decades of the century. Most of the smaller pits of the previous century were shut and development of new collieries at Norton Hill, Dunkerton and Pensford, on a larger scale than anything before, was begun. The increase in coalfield output was due primarily to the contribution made by these three pits up to the 1920s.

Against this, the new century saw some long-established pits vanish into history. Greyfield, the largest pit of its day, closed in 1911 and Huish followed in 1912. Edford closed in 1915 and the last of the famous Timsbury group closed in the following year. The depression and 1921 strike caused the closure of Farrington and Clutton, while the 1920s and early 1930s saw the abandonment of Dunkerton, Clandown, Priston, Middle Pit, Newbury and Moorewood. Ownerships changed and Sir Frank Beauchamp's Somerset Collieries Ltd began its climb to supremacy.

By the mid-thirties, therefore, the position had stabilised. Thirteen production units remained, comprising twelve coal-drawing shafts and two drift mines. All these units except Mells would survive until 1947 and nationalisation, though, of Old Mills and Springfield, only the latter would survive as a coal-winding shaft.

The following table shows the state of the coalfield in 1925:[12]

Coal raised	919,501 tons
Coal for colliery consumption	74,860 tons
Miners' free coal	27,182 tons
Coal commercially disposable	817,460 tons
Average proceeds per ton of coal	18s 1d
Total number of manshifts worked (underground)	1,098,538
Total number of manshifts worked (overall)	1,335,875
Output per manshift (OMS) at coal face	30.35cwt
OMS overall	13.77cwt

Costs per ton of coal raised:
Wages	12s 5d
Timber and pitwood	8.55d
Materials and stores	11.93d
Rents, royalties and wayleaves	7.56d

Remuneration of managers, directors, etc.	5.87d
Colliery wagon charges (including repairs)	8.06d
Total costs (excluding wages and minor expenses)	4s 11d

Overall results:

Trading profit for the year	7.8d per ton
Total profit	£29,911
Total proceeds from coal sales	£813,538

Several points from these figures deserve amplification. The OMS for the coalfield remained static, even falling slightly, which compares unfavourably with the national picture:

Year	OMS (Somerset)	OMS (National)
1927	16.85cwt	20.47cwt
1933	16.38cwt	22.67cwt
1939	15.95cwt	23.51cwt

This in itself is a measure of the lack of progress made in Somerset mining techniques when compared with the national picture. If we look at the use of machinery underground, a similar picture emerges:[13]

	1930	1935	1940	1943	1944
Number of mines using coal-cutting machines	2	3	4	4	3
Number of machines in use	5	6	7	5	8
Percentage of coal raised that was cut by machine	10	9	6	7	9
Number of mines using conveyors and loading machines	3	4	4	7	7
Percentage of total coal raised that was moved by machines	13	14	12	28	36

It can be seen from this that, while there was a slight increase in the number of coal-cutting machines in use in the coalfield during this period, this increase was accompanied by a *fall* in the percentage of the total coal that they cut. With conveyors and loaders the picture is the same up to World War II when, with the departure of men for the armed forces, machines were successfully used to fill the gaps.

On the credit side, however, a steadily decreasing labour force was still capable of producing a fairly constant amount of coal after 1930. The output for 1933 (695,380 tons) was produced by 3,532 men; in 1943 only 20,000 tons less was produced by 3,028 men, $2\frac{1}{2}$ per cent less coal with nearly 15 per cent fewer men. The actual outputs for the coalfield between 1930 and 1944 were as follows:

Year	Tons raised	Year	Tons raised
1930	798,800	1938	738,197
1931	801,600	1939	719,998
1932	722,900	1940	720,026
1933	695,380	1941	675,492
1934	694,400	1942	672,805
1935	707,900	1943	672,111
1936	747,000	1944	637,682
1937	764,794		

In the financial year 1943-4, the total output was 664,800 tons, of which 49.8 per cent was sold to gas works, a class of consumer whose purchases were to decline drastically in later years; 29.5 per cent was sold for miscellaneous industrial uses, while 13.1 per cent was sold for house coal.

As a small isolated coalfield, it might be expected that Somerset would supply a predominantly local market, but its success in doing so was only partial. In 1943 the total coal requirement of the south-western counties (Cornwall, Devon, Somerset, Wiltshire and Gloucestershire) was 5,579,609 tons, of which the Somerset coalfield suppplied 566,989 tons or 10.2 per cent. The Bristol coalfield, from its one remaining pit, supplied 0.9 per cent (51,522 tons) of this requirement and in fact the bulk of the South-west's supplies came from the Midlands or South Wales.

Somerset lagged behind in coal preparation. In 1943, 53 per cent of the coal received no treatment other than hand picking and was sold as 'thro' coal'; 40 per cent was screened into large and small coal and less than 10 per cent was treated in dry cleaning or washing plants. Indeed, only two pits had such facilities, though Old Mills was in course of installing a washer.

The entries so far are mainly on the debit side, curable by capital or enterprise. Certainly the industry was slow to realise the need to modernise and thereby withstand competition from other coalfields. An anonymous coalowner, refusing in 1912 to grant a wage demand, gave competition as his reason.[14] It was, he said, impossible to raise coal prices to pay for increased wages because 'only last Saturday I saw three or four trucks of Cannock Chase coal being unloaded at Mells Station'.

There remained those factors that were substantially unalterable. In 1943, pumping was costing 8.79d per ton of coal raised, or £13,500 for the 241 million gallons of water removed. These were not heavy costs compared with other coalfields, but were another cause of small profits.

Royalties and wayleaves were another cross that Somerset had to bear. Royalties varied between 6d and 9d per ton, 1d-3d higher than other coalfields. In 1925, 87 per cent of coal in Somerset was being mined under leases giving the landowner 4d-8d per ton; the remaining 13 per cent came from areas with a royalty of 1s per ton or more. It was, in part, to sort out inequalities of this sort that Government bodies were set up. The Coal Mines Reorganisation Commission was constituted under the Coal Mines Act of 1930 and, after its partial failure, was replaced by the Coal Commission. Formed under the Coal Act of 1938, with the object of unifying coal royalties in its own hands, this body likewise failed to equalise royalties.[15]

Before leaving this subject we may mention the term 'freeshare', which appears to be peculiar to Somerset. It occurs as early as 1659 and has been said to be interchangeable with the word 'royalty'. This is not strictly true. Certainly the older books of the Camerton Collieries recording these payments are entitled 'Freeshare' whereas the later books are entitled 'Royalty', but there is a difference, as an example will show.[16] At Camerton in 1921, 4,084 tons of coal were mined under land leased from Sir Frank Beauchamp; 5 per cent of this weight was, by the terms of the lease, deducted for colliery consumption, but on the remaining 3,879 tons Sir Frank was credited with a royalty of 6d per ton, ie £97. The average selling price of the coal was 29s 5½d per ton, which totals £5,714 14s. On this value, Sir Frank was credited with his freeshare of one-twentieth, ie £285 14s. However, from this sum was deducted the £97 royalty payment so that Sir Frank actually received £188 14s. In earlier days the usual rate of freeshare was an eighth or a tenth, which represented a good source of income for the mineral lords.

After the mid-1930s there were fourteen pits owned by seven separate companies. In 1941, production targets were given to each company and these give a good idea of their relative sizes.[17]

	Target (tons per week)	Number of men
Somerset Collieries Ltd★	5,870	1,140
Writhlington Collieries Ltd★★	2,370	601
Old Mills and New Mells	2,350	510
Pensford & Bromley	2,300	492
New Rock	800	175
Marsh Lane	130	43
Charmborough	110	31

★ Working four collieries
★★ Working two collieries

Excluding Marsh Lane and Charmborough, these figures represent an output per man of between 3.94 tons and 5.14 tons per week. If we look back to the 1890s, when output per man averaged about 4 tons per week,[18] the lack of progress over the intervening fifty years is very marked. The two highest targets per man, Norton Hill and Pensford, reflect the modern high capacity shafts at those pits. It is curious that the Writhlington target was so low and that New Rock, with its tiny single shaft, had such a high estimated capacity.

At the end of World War II the coal industry was nationalised. Whatever else, the National Coal Board was to provide a massive and long overdue injection of capital.

After 1947, the main concern of the private companies was the compensation that they would receive for their nationalised collieries. A sum of £597,000 was allocated to Somerset and the coalowners met in 1950 to decide how best to divide

it.[19] Two meetings failed to reach agreement but the money
was eventually divided as follows:

Somerset Collieries Ltd	£250,244
Wm Evans (Old Mills Collieries) Ltd	£138,816
Pensford & Bromley Collieries (1921) Ltd	£85,760
Writhlington Collieries Ltd	£60,000
New Rock Colliery Co Ltd	£40,247
Charmborough Collieries Ltd	£12,532
Marsh Lane Colliery	£9,401

NATIONALISATION

On 1 January 1947 the era of private mining in Somerset came
to an end. What exactly did the NCB inherit? In all, twelve
working mines: in the Mendips there were New Rock and
Charmborough; in the Radstock area there were Norton Hill,
Braysdown, Writhlington, Kilmersdon, and Ludlows; and
Springfield, Marsh Lane, Camerton, Pensford and Bromley
completed the picture. All were suffering from the effects of
the war, with neglected maintenance and labour shortages.
Norton Hill and Pensford were both opened in the twentieth
century but the rest had been operative for between seventy
and 150 years. The two drifts at Marsh Lane and Charmborough were less than thiry years old but were not important as
production units. Most pits, except Ludlows, had sufficient
coal reserves for the foreseeable future, but the quality and
accessibility of these reserves was expected to decline. It was
stated: 'There is a danger that the increasing difficulties will
render some of the collieries unworkable economically long
before their reserves are exhausted, unless steps are taken to
re-model them . . .'[20]

As a whole, the coalfield had accessible reserves that would
allow an annual production of 750,000 tons up to the year
2047. Some of the pits had an estimated life of only a few more
years; indeed, the closure of Ludlows had been anticipated in
the early 1940s. The first action of the NCB was to remove
some of the more obvious 'dead wood'. Charmborough was
closed immediately, Marsh Lane in 1949 and Camerton in
1950. Ludlows survived possibly longer than expected, closing
in 1954. However, Somerset had its share of the nationwide

demand for coal in the post-war years; output was maintained and a modest exploratory boring programme was begun.

A total of nineteen boreholes was put down, with a combined depth of over 4 miles, in areas that were either considered promising or little known.[21] Nine holes were put down in north-east Bristol and a new mine at Harry Stoke was opened as a result. The Avonmouth coal basin was explored with five holes and two 5ft thick seams discovered. The remainder of the boreholes were put down in Somerset, in the Ston Easton-Winford area, to try and prove the western extent of the coalfield. The coal proved by these was faulted and not workable.

The only tangible addition to the Bristol and Somerset coalfield was, therefore, the Harry Stoke mine, which, in the event, proved a failure. In Somerset, attention was concentrated on putting the existing pits into good order and planning the necessary modernisation. First steps were taken in 1949-50 with the approval of a £500,000 development scheme at Norton Hill, and within a few years other schemes of varying scope were begun at other pits considered to have a good future. New screening plants and electric winding engines were prominent at first, followed by plans for coal ploughs and trunk conveyors. The only 'new' development was the reopening of Strap Colliery to replace coal winding at the ageing and inefficient New Rock shaft.

By 1959, only five pits—Norton Hill, Old Mills, New Rock, Writhlington and Kilmersdon—survived at work. Norton Hill, with massive expenditure already incurred, was still in the throes of rebuilding and did not yield a profit until 1962. Modernisation was not always an immediate success partly because the men were unfamiliar with the new equipment. A series of errors at Writhlington in 1965 prompted the exasperated comment: 'if we concentrate on some old fashioned pit work, we can achieve the desired result'.[22]

From the figures below we can gain an idea of the way things went after 1947:[23]

Year	Saleable output (tons)
1947	589,214 (i)
1948	619,098

1949	634,222 (ii)
1950	529,009 (iii)
1951	532,476
1952	556,453
1953	554,865
1954	612,139 (iv)
1955	590,643
1956	615,658 (v)
1957	624,467 (vi)
1958	690,827 (vii)
1959	633,415
1960	612,124
1961	531,991
1962	619,176
First quarter 1963★	165,846
1963-64	560,723
1964-65	443,000
1965-66	425,972
1966-67	315,802 (viii)

★ A change was made at this time to the system of calculating outputs on the basis of the financial rather than the calendar year.

(i)   Charmborough Colliery closed
(ii)   Marsh Lane Colliery closed
(iii)   Camerton Colliery closed
(iv)   Ludlows Pit closed
(v)   Braysdown Colliery closed
(vi)   Bromley Colliery closed
(vii)   Pensford Colliery closed
(viii) Norton Hill and Old Mills collieries closed

Several things arise from these figures. The saleable output for 1947 was 99.6 per cent of the total coal raised; in 1963-64, the figure was 87.1 per cent. This reflects an increase in coal preparation plant in the coalfield. The main point is that, up to 1964, district output was held more or less constant despite the closure of four major collieries. There was a drastic drop in output after that date. Up to 1964 the figures surely show the beneficial effects of modernisation, which had enabled the output of twelve pits to be produced by five. But what happened after 1964?

The story is a familiar one. A nation that had demanded

coal suddenly turned round and refused it. Throughout the country the industry was thrown into confusion. In the Forest of Dean, Somerset's old rival, all nationalised mining ceased. The pits in Durham, South Wales, Lancashire and Scotland were all decimated and only the Midlands and Yorkshire flourished. Alternative fuels—gas from Algeria and the North Sea, imported oil, nuclear power—were in vogue and, to save the industry, it was necessary to concentrate resources on the largest and most productive areas. Somerset, which faced a severe shortage of manpower and an almost complete cessation of recruitment, could not be classed in either of these categories.

For Somerset, indeed, the national *volte-face* was disastrous. Nuclear power stations sprang up beside the coalfield. At Avonmouth, once a potential colliery site, a new gas works using liquified gas was built. The largest single market for Somerset coal became Portishead Power Station, at the mouth of the River Avon, and production was aimed at this. The coal ploughs cut small coal specially for Portishead.

The first casualties in Somerset were Norton Hill and Old Mills. Norton Hill, on which so much money had been expended and on which such hope had been fixed, went on to single-shift working in 1964 in an effort to stem the mounting losses which, other than for a brief period in 1962, had been almost continuous. Old Mills was closed to release men for work at other pits, the lack of recruits making this move essential. In 1968 New Rock was closed; the reasons were a complex of financial and labour difficulties. As at Norton Hill, large sums of money had been spent on modernisation, which, in all probability, never had a chance to pay for itself.

Since 1968, therefore, the Bristol & Somerset Group of the NCB has been working just two collieries—Writhlington and Kilmersdon. Under the control of the East Wales Area, these interlinked pits continue to supply Portishead and, at times, to flourish as they did in former days. Their combined output after 1964 has been around 250,000 tons per year, which is fair nationally but very good by Somerset standards.

It is impossible to predict when these pits might close. Many guesses have been made, but the pits are still here. Thus the tradition of Somerset coalmining lingers on, a blend of modern techniques and 'old fashioned pit work'. In 1969 an attempt was made, which may yet succeed, to open a small licensed drift mine in the coalfield. Perhaps, after the nationalised mines have gone, there will still be a group of Somerset miners working their coal and keeping alive a tradition of nearly 2,000 years.

THE MEN

What sort of men were the colliers of Somerset? It depended to a great extent upon the eye of the beholder. Warner in 1799 speaks of the 'dingy tenants of the coal mines' who were making Radstock ring 'with curses and vociferations'. There are many similar reports of drunkenness, lawlessness and disorder among the colliers. However, the other side of the picture is probably more accurate. William Smith found the miners both civil and helpful, as well as being knowledgeable about geology. John Wesley's evangelical tours in the coalfield after 1745 caused him to use adjectives such as earnest, honest, plain, simple and serious about the colliers.[24] Of course they got drunk at times, but they were by no means the only offenders, and the civilising influences of schooling and welfare work in the 1800s undoubtedly improved matters. By 1884, Morgans was able to declare that, for general sobriety, the men would compare with any in Great Britain. 'The bailiffs and overmen are nearly always recruited from the ranks of the colliers, and are a very superior class of men.'

As early as 1864 there was said to be a 'great clamour' for a miners' union and the result was that the Somersetshire Miners' Association was set up in 1872. Under the leadership of its agent, S. H. Whitehouse, the union began to grow, though it was not until 1937 that its membership included all the miners.

As for industrial relations, the Somerset miners of the mid-eighteenth century were involved in several food riots, but it should, in fairness, be pointed out that other groups of workers, such as weavers, were at least as lawless, though usually fewer in number and less well organised. One of the earliest disturbances was in August 1792 when some 4,000 colliers marched to complain about wages. The owners heard the men out and met their demands.

In February 1817 a 10 per cent wage reduction caused a more serious disturbance which required the Royal Lancers and the North Somerset Yeomanry to control it. However, these were very mild troubles. Other local colliers—the men from Kingswood district of Bristol, for example—were a much wilder lot. In 1738, sixty of them were arrested after sacking public houses, indulging in mass highway robbery and forcing the 'civilised colliers' of Brislington to join them.[25] As the years passed, strikes became more peaceful. In 1850, 100 Radstock men struck for higher wages but their conduct was orderly throughout. There were strikes in 1874, 1889 and 1893, the last two each lasting over four months. The Radstock strike of 1904 lasted from July into September and was one of the first in which the men received support from other trade unions:[26] the Northwich Salt Workers, the Cardiff Coal Trimmers and many others provided funds. Perhaps in gratitude to the North Wales quarrymen, who had also sent help, the Somerset union embarked upon a money-making venture called the Co-operative Quarries Pioneer Society in North Wales in the hope that profits from the quarries could be used to build up union funds; but after a few years the scheme failed miserably.

Undoubtedly the most bitter strike of recent times was that at Dunkerton in 1909, during which a number of miners were shot (see p121). Even so, it pales into insignificance when compared with the appalling battles fought during the strikes in South Wales during 1912. In Somerset, the 1912 strike passed peacefully and resulted in the men obtaining some concrete benefit, namely the Mines Minimum Wage Act. Finally the 1926 strike can be mentioned. The Somerset men had no special grievances and came out mainly through loyalty to the national Federation, and remained out until a settlement came at the end of 1926. One man tried to break the strike at Middle Pit in August but the reception he received from his fellow workers proved to be a very effective deterrent.[27]

Page 33 (above) Sinking operations at Pensford Colliery in about 1912. Note the temporary wooden headgear; *(below)* the new drift at Burchells Colliery nearing completion on 14 June 1909. The B & NSR is in the background

Page 34 Greyfield Colliery c 1900. From left to right: wooden headgear; Cornish engine house; winding engine house

United action—in strikes and otherwise—was a product of the strong local tradition of coalmining. Throughout the centuries it was Somerset men who worked their own mines. The lack of 'immigration' from other mining areas, other than in management, contributed to the tradition and also to a dearth of new ideas and methods. A close knit family tradition grew up, with sons following their fathers into the pits. So, too, in ownership, where the same names—Mogg, Rees-Mogg, Palmer, Crang, Adams—occur again and again. Only in this present century have the names of 'outsiders' appeared and even these often came from no further away than Bristol.

Unlike his Welsh counterpart, the Somerset miner was no great singer and only two miners' songs, both the products of strikes, are known. These are given below: [28]

> Onward ye brave miners, forward as to war,
>   Battles are not fought without an honest scar,
> Tyrants must be punished, blacklegs made to run,
>   The future's bright before us, if firmly we press on.

Chorus
>   Forward be our watchword, let us all unite,
>   And bravely fight for Whitehouse*, for Union and
>   for Right.
> *Whitehouse was the miners' agent

This song, sung to the tune of 'Onward, Christian Soldiers' during the 1889 strike, contains a reference in a later verse to keeping the law. This same theme is found in the second song, 'The Dunkerton Carting Boys', which was sung to an unknown tune and served as a rallying cry during the infamous riots at Dunkerton in 1909:

> The men and boys of the Dunkerton pit,
>   Came out on strike you see,
> For one 'alf-penny,
>   And mean to have that 'd'.
> They won't go back till they've got the advance,
>   And won the victory:
> So boys—join in—sing this song with glee:

Chorus
>   We're the Dunkerton carting boys,

C

Just the Dunkerton carting boys,
We're the Dunkerton carting boys,
  Oh! So true;
Tho' we're poorly and plainly dressed,
  We're as honest as one of the best,
We'll all stick together, whatever the weather,
  The Dunkerton Carting boys.

Somerset was rather an unhealthy coalfield to work in, having an incidence of silicosis and pneumoconiosis second only to South Wales. The reason was possibly the amount of stone blasting necessary in the thin Somerset seams. The health problem was so serious that, by the 1930s, the colliery companies would accept a man for work only with medical approval.[29]

The first colliery canteens did not appear until 1941 but within two years all pits except Marsh Lane and Charmborough had been so equipped. Most collieries did not get pithead baths until after nationalisation. As in other coalfields, conditions could be measured by absenteeism. In 1930, 5.1 per cent of the total possible manshifts were lost through avoidable absence; and in 1944, the figure was 11.2 per cent. Even this does not fully reflect the damage caused by absenteeism, affecting as it does primarily the younger coal-face workers. In 1944, 16.8 per cent of the total labour force in Somerset (2,984 men) was over the age of 55 and younger workers were thus seriously needed.[30]

In the old days, a youth in North Somerset had a choice of work—mining or agriculture. The agricultural worker worked in the open air for seven days a week; in winter, a coal-miner might not see the sun for six days but he would have the seventh off. Most went for the life of a miner, augmenting their wages during the summer short-time working in the pits by going on to the land. Perhaps this explains why every other house in the coalfield seems, even today, to be occupied by a miner or former miner. Each will speak strongly of the guss and crook, and each will say that his pit had 'the best coal in Somerset'. This loyalty to the coalfield, to the mines, and to the Somerset terminology, makes the Somerset miner a remarkable individual, and will survive long after the pits themselves are gone.

MINES AND COMMUNITIES

It is instructive to consider the growth of the coalfield in relation to the changes in population of the various mining
villages and parishes as revealed in the official ten-yearly cen-
sus reports. In 1831, there were about twenty mining parishes
housing a collier population of 1,855 or nearly 20 per cent of
the total male population. Paulton and Timsbury parishes had
a third of their men working in the mines, but in an area such
as Compton Dando or Farmborough the figure was only 5 per
cent, a matter of 20-50 men.

The total population of a parish was, in general, closely
related to the fortunes of its mines. An extreme example is
Farmborough. Here the total population in 1801 was 532; by
1841, when Farmborough Colliery was sinking, the figure had
doubled to 1,149. However, the failure of the enterprise by the
end of that decade caused the number of inhabitants to drop
to around 850, a level which was maintained until World
War II.

A more sustained example is to be found in Camerton
parish, where the 1801 population of 594 had risen to 1,543 in
1851, and to 2,386 by 1911, almost solely due to the considerable stability of employment provided by the Jarretts' Camerton Colliery.

Paulton in 1801 had 1,019 inhabitants, a figure that had
more than doubled by 1851. This increase was due almost
solely to the high wages paid at the collieries, the money allowing the men to marry much earlier than usual. However, by
1860 most of the pits were shut and the population level decreased, only to rise again by 1871 with the sinking of Old
Mills and Springfield collieries. These pits, also reliable em-
ployers, belong economically to Midsomer Norton rather than
Paulton but much of their labour came from the latter parish.

There are marked examples of a decline in population with
the closure of the collieries. Thus Holcombe, one of the Mendip parishes, lost a third of its inhabitants between 1801 and
1861, while High Littleton declined from 1,116 persons in
1841 to 740 in 1871. Many of the mining families moved to
South Wales and the North of England during the 1860s and

this migration explains similar population declines at Farm-borough, Timsbury and Camerton during the same period.

The centre of the coalfield was—and is—the urban district of Norton-Radstock, an amalgam of Midsomer Norton and Radstock. The former area, which included the rich Duchy of Cornwall mines at Welton, had three times the population of Radstock in 1801 (1,552 to 509 persons) but both experienced uninterrupted growth throughout the nineteenth century until, by 1901, there was a combined population of nearly 10,000. Thereafter there was little net increase and the 1961 figure was only 12,793. The natural growth of the community was balanced by the migration to other coalfields as the Welton and Radstock pits declined. Indeed, so great was this exodus that, for the expansion of Norton Hill Colliery in the 1950s, miners had to be induced to move into Somerset from South Wales and Durham.

So far we have said nothing about the mobility of labour within the coalfield, a problem which can only be given a brief mention here. There are several instances of ranks of new houses being erected to house the workmen of a new mine, the village around Kilmersdon Colliery being an example. For the older pits, however, the men seem to have integrated into existing communities without obvious rows of miners' cottages. These men would often own their own homes and, when their local pit closed, be reluctant to move. Instead, they would be content to travel further to work. The men for the new Dunkerton Colliery came from all over the northern region of the coalfield. Such daily travelling was accentuated as the coalfield contracted and even today there are men who travel 10 miles from Pensford to Kilmersdon for work.

Today, although about 600 people are still dependent on the two remaining collieries, the area as a whole is not. New light industry, and the functions of dormitory towns and villages for Bristol and Bath, have replaced mining as the prime factor in community growth.

Notes begin on page 265.

2 TECHNICAL BACKGROUND TO THE COALFIELD

GEOLOGY

In order to understand the history of the coalfield it is necessary also to understand the geology of the area. The Bristol and Somerset Coalfield has a proven area of some 240sq miles and forms two asymmetric coal basins, each containing two major groups of coal seams (or veins as they are termed in Somerset). The Bristol and Somerset basins are virtually separated from each other by the east-west Kingswood Anticline in Bristol and thus the Somerset portion can be considered as a separate area.

The Somerset coal basin is greatly faulted, causing isolated coal tracts whose correlation is not fully understood. Such areas exist at Nailsea and Clapton, where some mining has taken place, though the economic and geological separation distinguishes these outliers from the main bulk of the coalfield. Even here, with less than 25 per cent of the total known area actually exposed at the surface and newer formations overlying the rest, the exact east and west boundaries of the coalfield are not known with certainty.

The coal seams fall into three distinct groups. The Upper Group (2,400ft thick at maximum) contains two series, the Radstock and Farrington series, which are separated by a bed of barren red shales. Next in descending order is the Middle or Pennant Group (2,000-2,500ft thick) which contains only one seam, the Rudge, which has been mined commercially, at Marsh Lane and in early workings. Finally, the Lower Group (3,000ft thick) contains two series of seams, the New Rock and Vobster series. There is no clear demarcation between these

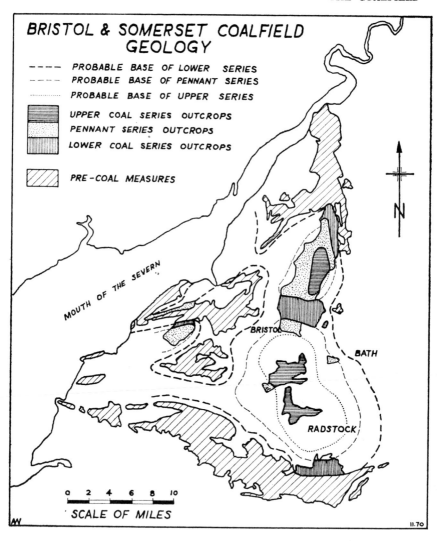

BRISTOL & SOMERSET COALFIELD GEOLOGY

series, the distinction being drawn mainly on the character of the coal. The Vobster seams have strong coking properties which the New Rock seams do not possess.

Radstock Series
This contains the Withy Mills, Great, Top Little, Middle, Slyving, Under or Bottom Little, Bull and Nine Inch seams,

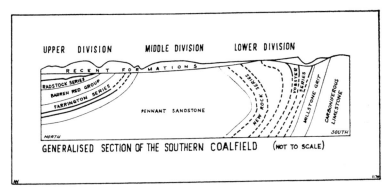

GENERALISED SECTION OF THE SOUTHERN COALFIELD   (NOT TO SCALE)

with an aggregate thickness of about 13ft 8in. The first seam is usually absent while the last is often unworkable. Seams in Somerset often have names evocative of their properties or other characteristics. For example, the Slyving derives from 'Sly Vein', meaning that the seam has an untrustworthy roof. The Radstock Series was last worked at Camerton Colliery in 1950.

Farrington Series
The seams of this series, named after Farrington Colliery, have a variety of designations at different pits. The old names —Cathead, Top, Peacock, Middle, New or Church Close, Seventeen Inch—have been superseded by a numbering system applicable to the entire coalfield. On the exhaustion of the Radstock Series, many shafts were sunk through the red measures to reach this series and the two remaining pits in Somerset both work Farrington Series coal.

New Rock Series
Twenty-five to thirty seams occur in the New Rock and Vobster series; they are thicker than those of the Upper Series but are usually of poorer quality. The series name derives from New Rock Colliery where these coals were first extensively worked, and where they were last worked in 1968.

Vobster Series
These seams, named after the village in whose area they out-

crop, were probably the first to be worked in Somerset. They yield good coking coal but are extremely difficult and dangerous to work, being fragmented, steeply graded (often vertical) and the most gaseous.

Faults and Contortions

The character of the coalfield is due primarily to disturbances caused by the upthrust of the Mendip Hills, one of a parallel series of east-west disruptions that stretches southwards into the Atlantic Ocean. Several major faults, usually of the slide or overlap type, have been produced, together with innumerable minor faults. The Farmborough Fault is one of the largest, being actually several great downthrow faults that cut off the coal north of Timsbury so that it is not seen again until the outcrops at Marksbury are reached. This fault has also cut off the Pensford basin and as a result the correlation of these seams is uncertain. Possibly the Pensford seams are equivalent to the Radstock Series and the Bromley seams to the Farrington. Another fault, the Radstock Slide Fault, bisects Radstock, as does a north-south fault running from Clandown Colliery possibly as far south as Newbury Colliery.

The greatest disturbance has been near the Mendips. Here, the Vobster seams appear to have acted as a wedge between the upthrusting hills and the bulk of the coalfield, the result being that the seams have been distorted to an amazing degree. In the west, the seams have their normal dip to the north but, proceeding eastwards, the dip becomes steeper until the seams are vertical. Further east, the seams actually overturn and dip *southwards,* so that the roof of the seam becomes the floor. It is possible that, east of Mells, the seams again become vertical and resume their northern dip, but this is not proved.

THE MINES

Collieries in Somerset were very different from those of the larger coalfields in the country. Set amid rural greenery, they were seldom obtrusive, mainly because the building materials used in their construction—white, rough hewn, lias stone with grey slate roofing—made the surface works both neat and inconspicuous. Only the twentieth-century pits were built of red brick. In this section we shall look at the component parts of Somerset collieries and illustrate the use of mining terms both general to the industry and peculiar to Somerset.

Shafts

In some cases the need for shafts rather than adits arose as early as the 1400s and many were sunk on Kilmersdon and Stratton commons during that period. There was still scope for drift mines; indeed, there is to this day, and we may instance the new co-operative mines of this century (eg Marsh Lane), the currently proposed Common Wood Level, and the scheme to replace Writhlington and Kilmersdon shafts with a new drift that was proposed (and rejected) in the 1960s. When driving a level in the early days, it was usually possible to follow a coal seam; for sinking a shaft, it was necessary to predict the position and depth of the coal and in the 1600s a forked hazel-wood divining stick was considered a suitable tool for prospecting.[1] Even so, there was a good understanding of the principles of stratigraphy in practice, though it was two centuries before they were set down on paper.

Shaft depths varied with the need. At Clutton in 1610 the deepest of three shafts was 48ft, while at Perthill on Stratton Common there were shafts over 60ft deep at the same period. In the 1690s, George Stedman's pit at Stratton is said to have been 420ft deep, though this is possibly erroneous.[2] By the 1790s, however, depths had increased considerably; in the northern part of the coalfield 500ft or more was not uncommon, while in the Mendips perhaps half this depth was more usual. By 1817, Clandown Colliery shaft was over 1,200ft deep, a record for the time.

This was the era of mining in areas with thick superficial deposits covering the coal measures and the pattern was increasingly one of deeper new sinkings and deepening of existing shafts. The deepest shaft ever sunk in Somerset was at Downside Colliery which reached 1,838ft in the 1870s, but once this pit had closed in 1879 the record was held by Braysdown (1,740ft by 1862) and Middle Pit (1,791ft in 1886).

The diameter of these shafts, which were almost always circular, was very peculiar to Somerset. For centuries a diameter of 4ft was common, increased to 4ft 6in or 5ft by the 1800s. New Rock wound all its coal up a shaft 1,182ft deep and 4ft 6in diameter well into NCB times, as did Bromley up to 1957. One cannot help admiring the skill of the early miners, who could sink so deep a shaft with such a tiny diameter.

Wider shafts were necessitated by the introduction of cages and guides in the 1850s and it must be assumed that all shafts up to this time were of the small size, though in most cases no widening dates are known. Because of this small diameter it was common practice to have two shafts at each colliery and Somerset was thus in a favourable position when, after the Hartley disaster in 1862 in the North of England coalfield, legislation making two shafts compulsory was introduced. If a single shaft was wide enough, as at Old Mills and Downside, it might be divided by brattices (partitions) into two halves, an upcast side (for foul air leaving the pit) and a downcast (for fresh air entering), one side of the brattice being used for pumping and the other for winding.

Ventilation

Although most Somerset collieries were free from any explosive gases, some means of passing an air current through the workings was nonetheless desirable. Usually a mechanical aid was required, normally a furnace, the rising current of hot air so produced drawing air round the workings. Furnace ventilation was common in the county into the present century but fans are now in use.

Systems of Winding

From the earliest days coal was wound up the shaft by a horse gin, the coal being carried in a wicker basket or corve. Concurrent with the introduction of steam winding was the installation of hudges (iron tubs or barrels), holding anything up to a ton of coal. Corves were used here and there up to the 1870s, doubtless in the smaller Somerset pits, but the more advanced mines took early advantage of the economies presented by the hudge. The records of Paulton Foundry show that hudges were still in use in several pits in the 1860s but by this time cages, guides and wheeled coal-tubs were rapidly being introduced in Somerset.

It is frequently stated that Somerset was a backward area mechanically, and the late introduction of cages and guides is usually given as an example. In point of fact, Somerset was not so laggard as is generally supposed. In 1816 the first experiments with cages and guides were made in Co Durham and it was under the auspices of T. Y. Hall that a successful system was introduced in 1836 on the Tyne. Double the amount of coal could now be raised in a given time and by the 1850s the system was in general use. This is precisely the decade of the first successful applications in Somerset, though it was not until the late 1860s that these devices became common.[3] Admittedly this is slightly later than in other coalfields but the reasons are obvious. The narrow shafts had first to be widened to cope with cages and guides and it was not until 1874 that there was a fairly complete railway network. There was little point in doubling output if no way existed to dispose of the additional coal!

Winding Engines

Somerset quickly standardised on the conventional two-cylinder horizontal type of engine with a parallel drum; a common size was about 26in x 60in cylinders and a 12ft diameter drum. There were, of course, a variety of early grotesque experiments. One of the earliest was at Upper Conygre, which by 1795 is said to have had a dual engine in the sense that it could be converted for winding by day and pumping by night. A similar arrangement probably operated at Huish, where the Bond pumping engine was converted to a winder in 1823.[4] In 1800 a winding engine was erected at Old Pit by an engineer named Jeffreys, but, 'being of imperfect construction, it did not remain long in use'.[5] In 1804, a highly successful engine was erected at Middle Pit, increasing output to 50 tons per day.[6]

Few collieries had electric winding engines. The first was probably that at Mells Colliery in about 1938-40 and they were installed by the NCB at all their latter-day pits. The New Rock shaft was the last to be worked by steam, an electric engine being installed a few months before its closure in 1968.

Man Riding

The earliest system, still in use at Nettlebridge in the 1860s, was the 'hooker' system, commonly compared to a string of onions;[7] a man would sit in a loop of rope hooked on to the winding rope and if one imagines a dozen men riding in this fashion, the analogy is obvious. Each man, often carrying a boy on his lap, would hold on to the rope with one hand while fending himself off from the sides of the shaft with his free hand. The other system in use before cages was a man hudge, a coal hudge with a hole in one side and a roof, in which two or three men could be wound at once.

Winding Ropes

The old style of rope, a flat hemp rope woven from several smaller strands, was susceptible to both decay and breakage (as at Paulton Engine in 1830) and to malicious damage such as occurred at Wellsway in 1839 when twelve persons were killed. Wire ropes. either round or flat in section, were introduced along with cages, and at Lower Conygre Colliery a flat wire rope $3\frac{1}{2}$in wide and $\frac{3}{4}$in thick, and woven from twenty-one $\frac{1}{4}$in diameter strands, was in use up to 1916. By this time, however, round ropes were usual, and a more recent development, the locked coil rope, is in use today.

Drainage

The early adits were driven into hillsides so that water could drain away by gravity. After 1780, special drainage levels were driven to serve groups of mines, as at Timsbury and those collieries served by the Edford and Benter complex of levels at Nettlebridge. Steam pumping came in after 1750, on which date the first engine is popularly supposed to have been introduced at Paulton Engine Colliery.[8] The beam type of engine, atmospheric at first and later of the Cornish type, survived at some pits into this century, but the tendency was to use tanks slung in or under the cages for removing water from the sump of the shaft. When fitted with automatic filling and emptying devices, such tanks were economical in use. As early as 1864, at the Radstock Collieries: 'the inconsiderable feeder of water [which] used to occupy six pumping engines and about a mile of pumps . . . is now raised in a few hours by means of water tanks'.[9]

Increasingly after 1900, electric pumps were installed and today perform all pumping operations.

Methods of Working

Because the coal seams of Somerset are thin, steep and faulted, specialised methods of working the coal have been evolved.[10] Broadly speaking there are two methods of coalmining in the country, each subject to innumerable local variations: pillar and stall, and longwall. In the former method, only part of the coal is extracted, the rest being left as pillars to support the roof. It was formerly common in the main coalfields of this country, being both an ancient and wasteful method. In Somerset, longwall methods have been generally used.

In this system all the workable coal is extracted along a single working face, which can be several hundred yards in length. This method had the disadvantage that a large amount of timber was needed to support the roof in lieu of pillars, and in Somerset pitwood might constitute up to 15 per cent of the total expenditure on materials. The longwall method is today fairly general with the NCB and it is thus of interest to note that in this instance Somerset was a pioneer.

Pillar and stall was used, however, at the Nailsea pits in 1869 and was tried at Radstock in the same period, 'with only indifferent success'. It was also used in certain special situations, such as the Great Course Vein at New Rock Colliery, into NCB times. In this case, when the workings reached a maximum in any one area, the pillars would be progressively extracted, thus removing all the coal from the area. We can now consider the working of a 'typical' Somerset colliery.

To obtain an economic output it was not only necessary to work longwall but also to work several seams simultaneously, for which purpose the winding shaft might have one or more intermediate levels. From the bottom of the shaft at the colliery described by Presto in 1884, an incline or 'ducky' (corruption of the term 'dukeway'), which was laid with a single line of tub rails (called a 'crease'), ran downwards at an angle of 1 in 3. At the foot of the dukeway was a road running at right-angles and leading to a 'standing', where coal from the workings was loaded into tubs. This road ran into the heart of the mine and was called a 'twinway' (ie [be]tween way), being more or less level.

Coal could reach the twinway by two routes: if it was being mined to the rise (at a higher level than the twinway) it would be let down a self-acting incline known as a 'gugg'. The coal travelled in a wooden box fitted with runners like a sledge and known as a 'putt'. If, on the other hand, coal was being mined to the dip of the twinway, each putt was mounted on a four-wheeled carriage and pushed up by the carting boy. It was the carting boys' duty to haul the putts back and forth to the coal-getters at the faces. All putts arriving at the twinway would be loaded on to carriages and pushed along rails to the standing, where the coal would be tipped out into tubs and the carriage and empty putt taken back to their respective starting points.

This can be imagined as a simple dichotomous system: the twinway branches into guggs and dipples; these in turn would be fed by secondary twinways; and finally puttways would connect to the coal faces. Puttways, if very steep, were fitted with static ropes, anchored at both ends, and were then called 'topples'. To work a putt on a topple was a skilled and dangerous job: the full putt was run astride the rope which, being slack, could then be wound round the crook of an instrument known as the 'guss and crook'.

More than anything else, the 'guss and crook' was the hallmark of Somerset mining, and its memory is among the most indelible in the coalfield. The device will be discussed below; suffice it to say here that it consists of a circle of 1in diameter tarred rope worn round the waist of the carting boy, and from the front of the rope hangs a chain about 15in long with a hook or crook shaped in an elongated 's' attached to the other end. In use the carting boy would hook the crook to an eye on the putt and crawl off on all fours, with the chain running between his legs, dragging the putt behind him.

On the topple, therefore, the rope was wrapped round the crook, which was then hooked to the putt. The putt was pushed down the topple, being restrained by the friction of the rope on the crook and by the carting boy's own strength. This was potentially a dangerous task; so, too, was working a putt, on its carriage, up a dipple to the twinway. Two boys would normally be involved in this work, one pulling with the guss and crook and the other pushing from behind with his head. The peril in this, if one boy were to lose his footing, can easily be seen. It was equally dangerous to work a loaded putt down a topple not fitted with a static rope; if the boy were to lose his grip, he would be dragged downhill behind the runaway putt. It is surprising how few accidents would result from these methods when a boy became skilled at his duties. Twinway work, on easy gradients that could be used for a rest period by riding on the free-wheeling carriage, was less demanding.

The methods of working described above were traditional in Somerset but were, in recent times, by no means universal. In pits favoured by good conditions or enlightened management, horses could be substituted for boys in the twinway at least—it might even be possible to bring tubs up to the faces, thus eliminating much of the guss work. James McMurtrie is to be credited with the first serious attempts to introduce these new methods, which, apart from humane considerations, were more economical. 'Formerly,' says McMurtrie, 'there was a great want of method' in Somerset mining, the exact mode of working depending on the whim of the bailiff in charge. After 1863 McMurtrie introduced a regular system of mining, depending on adequate exploration, to a plan prepared beforehand and superimposed upon a surface map. Underground, his modifications greatly shortened the human haulage and cut costs by reducing the length of roadway to be kept in repair. He further introduced the self-acting incline to many topples, eliminating another source of danger and low output.

Such methods served in Somerset up to the 1930s, though as this century advanced they served progressively less well. However, with the technology of the nineteenth century, these were the only methods that could be applied in Somerset and, without them, little coal would have been produced.

Geology and the Economics of Mining

The local designation of a coal seam greater than 24in thick is a 'thick' seam, while thin seams go down to 12in or, rarely, even less. This may come as a surprise to those who only know other coalfields, in which a man can stand upright in the seam. In Somerset, coal has been worked in seams so thin that a man could not even lie sideways; the only way to win the coal was to lie on one's back and swing a small pick with one hand, pivoting the elbow on a board. There was no hope of using a shovel in such conditions and the coal would simply be kicked out with the feet. The difficulties of such conditions are apparent, as is the high cost that such working must entail. Admittedly such thin seams were only worked when nothing else was available, and a thickness of 20-30in would be nearer the average. Even so, this is a far cry from most other coalfields.

Because of these thin seams, a great quantity of rubbish and waste stone was produced; in 1881 it was said that a third of the total material raised from a colliery could be rubbish. To maintain a twinway even 4ft square in a 2ft seam means that a disproportionate amount of dead work—ripping away the floor or roof—is needed. Add to this the numerous faults, which mean uneven gradients, laborious exploration and costly stone-drifting before the coal is rediscovered, and it is obvious that Somerset collieries laboured under a combination of difficulties that would have been the despair of men from other coalfields. Undoubtedly one of the reasons for the reluctance of coalowners to spend money was their uncertainty about the possible returns of such collieries.

The Guss and Crook

Over the country as a whole, the guss and crook is a device

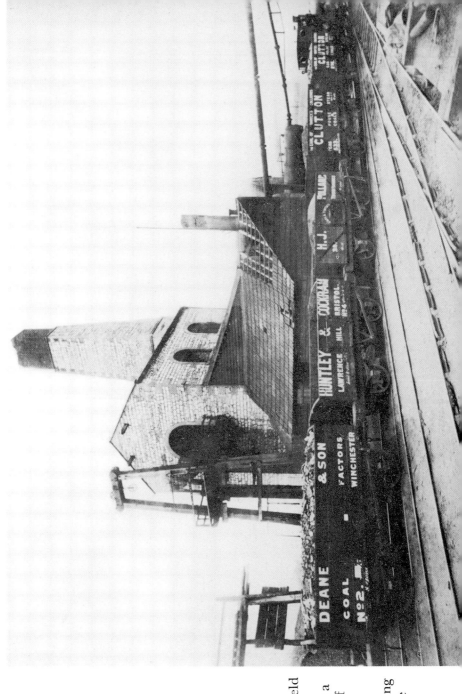

Page 51 Greyfield Colliery, with *Daisy* shunting a fine selection of private-owner wagons. The Cornish pumping engine is in the background

Page 52 Lower Conygre Colliery: *(above)* soon after completion of the surface rebuilding; *(below)* the eastern shaft, showing the three-deck cage and the peculiar design of the headgear

of fair antiquity with a variety of local names and designs. In Yorkshire the 'belt and chain' was common in the 1840s; in Derbyshire it was known as the 'dog belt'. With the introduction of coal tubs it was rapidly superseded except in Somerset and, to a lesser extent, in the Forest of Dean coalfield. It survived in Somerset in its original form up to the 1930s, and to 1949 at Marsh Lane.

The putts hauled by this means varied in size. In the Radstock area they were about 3ft long, 1ft 6in wide and 9-12in high, holding up to 1¾cwt of coal. In the Newbury area they were about 4ft long and held 2cwt. In every case the putt can be described as a wooden sledge, shod with iron, with the runners extended upwards to form sides and an extension at the rear to make a three-sided box, 5-8in deep.

It is not surprising that the continued survival of the guss and crook should have provided certain people with food for thought. In the 1880s voices were raised against it and in 1913 an unpublished report was prepared for the Home Office by Hugh Johnstone and Dr Edgar Collis. They commented that, while men engaged in guss work had a tendency to contract a disease known as 'beat knee', the guss had no harmful effects whatsoever. However, the subject was one better suited to emotion than reason, and passions were high during the 1926 strike with the columns of local newspapers filled with acrimonious correspondence about the guss and crook. Most letters were rather less than accurate but the guss became a symbol of tyrannical oppression and was used as such by the Miners' Association. A lady member of Parliament even went so far as to exhibit a guss, plus photographs of its use, during a debate in the House of Commons. Perhaps this had the desired effect: in July 1927 the Home Office appointed the Guss Committee, whose report was published in September 1928.[11]

The reason for the survival of the guss was quite simply that, since the seams were so thin, most owners wished to avoid the expense of roadways big enough to take tubs. But even where the seam was thick enough to allow tubs to be brought to the face, this was not usually done. The putt and guss, therefore, offered the one way of getting coal out from the faces.

D

The committee was struck by one undeniable fact, the effectiveness of the guss in enabling human power to be applied to a job of work. The guss, they said, 'must be adjudged a very efficient device', and commented on the speed with which a new carting boy learnt its technique.

Two points which occupied the committee were the question of personal injury arising from the use of the guss, and the objections raised by the union on behalf of the men. The latter were easily answered: the men were not only satisfied with the guss but resented any thoughts of doing away with it. Some expressed the view that, without the guss, the pits would be shut down as uneconomic, and perhaps an element of self-preservation does creep in here. However, the fact remains that the committee could find no man willing to express disapproval of the guss, despite the statements of the union to the contrary.

The most emotional subject was that of injuries sustained by the carting boys. Many persons, usually not miners, testified that carting boys could be seen after a day's work with blood running down their sides because of using the guss, but, here again, the truth was found to be very different. The only soreness and chafing due to the guss rope came when a carting boy was new to the job. Within a very few days this would pass entirely. Such events could often be attributed to the fact that the guss did not fit properly—a good fit was essential for comfort.

The one injury that was taken seriously was beat knee, an acute localised inflammation of the subcutaneous layers caused by the crawling involved in the work. Measured as incidence per thousand men employed, the highest national figure was 4.47, except in Somerset and the Forest of Dean where the figure was 15.5. In 1913, 42.5 per thousand Somerset carting boys had the disease.

There were other causes of injury arising from the use—or, more correctly, the misuse—of the guss, notably those back strains arising from the use of the guss in putting derailed tubs of coal back on the lines. This practice was strongly condemned. Despite the efficiency of the guss for its intended purpose, the committee concluded that the effort exerted was out of all proportion to the amount of coal moved and their recommendations were primarily concerned with improving this. They suggested ways of altering mining patterns to render the guss obsolete but admitted that this could only be a long-term solution. They proposed, therefore, that wheeled putts should be introduced. A pressed-steel putt designed at the Writhlington Collieries was found to be lighter than the traditional wooden type and, by reducing rolling resistance, enabled a greater amount of coal to be moved per journey with less exertion. Such putts were also tried at Old Mills Colliery but it was found that the wheels tended to cut into the floor, making matters worse than before. Generally, therefore, the traditional design remained in use.

Mining today

Kilmersdon and Writhlington collieries today have much in common with pits in other coalfields. Coal ploughs and face conveyors are used in conjunction with trunk conveyors which carry the coal to near pit bottom for loading into tubs. The coal travels in tubs only up the shaft and at the pithead. All the usual modern devices are installed: automatic banking, compressed air rams for loading tubs into the cages, and creepers and tipplers for automatic handling of tubs at the surface. All this equipment is to NCB standard designs. Mining methods are a far cry from those of but a few decades ago, but the pits will live out their time with their traditions and terminology as a continuing reminder of prouder days.

Notes begin on page 265.

3 THE NORTHERN OUTPOSTS

If the Somerset coalfield is a backwater among the coalfields of the country, then the Pensford coal basin occupies a similar position in Somerset. The pits included here possess several features of interest: Pensford, one of the newest and largest pits in Somerset, crippled by financial troubles in World War I; Farmborough, a sinking begun with great hopes, which never found coal; and Common Wood, the most recent venture, which is labouring under similar troubles. Every vicissitude to which the Somerset coalfield has been subject is to be found in the histories of the pits in this chapter.

THE BISHOP SUTTON COLLIERIES

During the last 250 years there have been many collieries in the area round Bishop Sutton; there was at least one pit in 1719 and four in 1750. One, that at Coalpit Farm, had a shaft 300ft deep, and another was known as Travis Pit after its owner. The age of Bishop Sutton Old Pit is uncertain; the first known lease was signed on 24 March 1811 and this lease was followed by other leases in 1817 and 1819.[1] Part of the pit's output was used by another ancient Somerset industry, lead smelting. The colliery was closed by about 1855.

In 1855, land at Bishop Sutton was bought by that famous mining partnership of John and William Rees-Mogg, Charles Hollwey and R. Lewis.[2] Sutton Old Colliery and the 'new pit site' are mentioned at this time, from which it can be inferred that Bishop Sutton New Pit was sunk about 1855. William Rees-Mogg purchased a pit (almost certainly Old Pit) on 17 May 1853 for £2,000.[3]

By 1880, J. G. and Samborne Cook were also partners in the Bishop Sutton Coal Co, John Rees-Mogg being no longer concerned. A new lease was taken on 20 July 1880 for 33 years but this was terminated by the partners on 25 March 1884 and a new lease was presumably obtained. In 1880 the colliery buildings were worth £506 and it had a steam winding engine and a Cornish-type pumping engine.[4]

The undertaking prospered in a small way; between November 1879 and February 1889, profits totalled £3,562 against losses of £557. The highest quarterly profit was £252 and the greatest loss £243. Dividends totalling £3,200 were paid out during this period.[5]

On 24 March 1889 working came to an abrupt halt when water broke into the workings and the pit was flooded. The partners estimated that it would take at least six months to pump out the water, at a cost of £16 per week. In addition, 20 tons of coal would have to be purchased each week at 7s 6d per ton, and it was decided to stop all pumping pending a report by J. Batey on whether or not the pit should be abandoned. Batey's report was not optimistic and on 14 June it was resolved to try and sell the colliery as a going concern. In this the partners were successful; in November 1889 the colliery, the site of the old colliery and the 'beer house' were sold to Frederick Spencer (of New Rock Colliery and Oakhill Brewery) for £2,120. Spencer bought more property for £1,350 at the same time, and retained the old trading title of the pit.

By 1914 the pit had changed hands again, the new owners being Jesse, Walter, Frederick, James, Ernest, Joseph and Arthur Lovell, who traded as the Bishop Sutton Colliery Co and employed about fifty men.[6] The pit had already survived longer than might have been expected, but by November 1924 at the latest it had changed hands again. For the last years of its life, it was owned by the Bishop Sutton Colliery Co Ltd with H. G. Godfrey-Peyton (of the Earl of Warwick's estates), Frank Hadley, H. Butler, T. E. Moody and F. Povey-Harper as directors.[7]

In November 1921, two-thirds of the employees (who then numbered about 120 men) were discharged but told that they would be reinstated if they accepted a 5 per cent cut in wages. During the previous three months, the owners had lost nearly £1,000 and they refused to risk any more money. However, the pit remained at work until it was closed down in May 1926, during the strike. The men offered to return to work as a co-operative partnership but this was refused and they were given their cards. Yet again, the pit survived and work resumed after the strike. Finally, in March 1929, 'the Bishop Sutton Company [was] hopelessly insolvent'; four months later, the company was in the hands of the receiver, with no assets, and the pit was never again worked.[8] Other than the dirt tips, which are soon to be built on, there are few traces of the colliery remaining today.

BROMLEY COLLIERY

Bromley Colliery is said to have started life as a well and, according to one source, was sunk at least as early as 1860. However, the earliest mention of the colliery is 1893 when it was owned by L. & N. Gibbs.[9]

In 1905 it was proposed that the Blagdon Light Railway

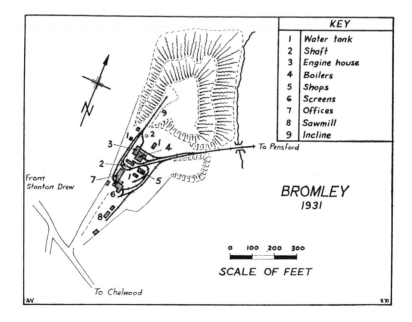

should be built and run from the terminus of the Wrington Vale Light Railway at Blagdon to the GWR near Pensford.[10] This railway, which was never built, would have passed to the north of the colliery and the company stated that they would put at least 1,000 tons of coal per week on the railway if they were served by a siding. Unless this was just a paper figure, it seems to be rather large for so small a colliery; for the maximum output known (in the 1930s) was only 1,100 tons per week.[11]

In 1909 proposals were made for the sinking of a new colliery at Pensford and in December of that year, ownership of Bromley passed from the Bromley Colliery Co into the hands of the Pensford & Bromley Collieries Ltd, with registered offices at Bromley. With the sinking of Pensford and memories of the abortive Blagdon Light Railway, the opportunity was taken to build a tramway from Bromley to the new colliery site and thereby gain access to the GWR. This tramway was of 2ft 0in gauge and ran in a straight line across the fields to Pensford, a distance of about a mile. The earthworks included several high embankments and deep cuttings, necessary to keep the gradients at an acceptable figure.

A steam locomotive was bought from the Avonside Engine Co in Bristol in 1910 to work traffic on the tramway.[12] It was a small, outside cylinder, $0-4-0$ side tank locomotive (works number 1593) and bore the name *Bromley No 1*, but unfortunately it proved to be both underpowered and prone to derailment. Accordingly, it was sold in 1913 to the Old Delabole Slate Co Ltd in Cornwall, which firm was not very pleased with it either, for it was resold by February 1915 to Harper Brothers & Co for use on construction works at the War Department's Catterick Camp.

The locomotive's successor was not another locomotive but a main-and-tail rope haulage system, by means of which sets of about fifty tubs were drawn along the tramway. Each tub held 7½cwt of coal and tared 3cwt 35lb, the smallest in Somerset, and a set would thus carry about 17 tons of coal.

In this form the tramway lasted until the closure of the pit. About 1937 the wooden bridge carrying the line over the

Stanton Drew – Stanton Wick road caught fire and collapsed, preventing the use of the line until it could be rebuilt. It is said that some of the local residents were not slow to salvage some free firewood! The tramway began with a short incline down from Bromley pithead, and then ran north-east to Pensford, where it passed over the Pensford – Stanton Wick road by a steel girder bridge and then ran up a gantry to Pensford screens. The main-and-tail engine was at first erected at Bromley, but was moved to Pensford about 1916.

The costs of working at Bromley were always high and there was also the expense—2d per ton in 1914—of taking the coal to Pensford. Even in 1914 it was recommended that the pit should be closed, and in 1922 it had an estimated life of only eight years.[13] Under the National Coal Board, therefore, closure was really only a matter of time. Modernisation was impossible underground because of the tortuous roadways, and the small size of the shaft prevented an increase in output. Gradually the pit was run down. In 1932 there were 230 employees, in 1946 there were 157, and in 1951 only 67 men remained. Output was the lowest in Somerset, about 10,000 tons in 1951. Bromley was also the last pit in Somerset to use horses for hauling tubs underground, four being in use in 1955. On 18 May 1957, coal winding ceased for ever.

The course of the tramway is visible today, though some of the bridges have been removed and cuttings filled in. There are still some rotting sleepers in the ground, as well as the old haulage rope lying in the hedge beside the track bed. Apart from the tip, there are few traces at the colliery, the site being now a vehicle repair depot. The capped northern shaft can still be seen, as can the bodies of one or two tipping wagons lying at the foot of the tip. A house has been built on the foundations of the landsale chutes; otherwise, there are no significant remains.

PENSFORD COLLIERY

Pensford was a twentieth-century pit and, as such, lacked some of the charm of the older pits of the coalfield. Built of red brick as opposed to white stone, the buildings were prominent on the hillside half a mile south of Pensford village. The huge tips were—and still are—conspicuous features of the area.

The earliest known lease was taken for a term of sixty years from 25 December 1909 and the sinking of two 14ft diameter shafts began in the following year. Appalling difficulties with water were encountered and in 1914 the work was still incomplete.[14] The south shaft had been sunk 750ft, but the sinking machinery on this shaft had been dismantled and there was then no way of continuing the work. At the north shaft, a depth of 1,494ft had been reached. Sinking here had ceased due to flooding and in March 1914 there was 1,300ft of water in the shaft. Pumping was costing £150 (and 120 tons of boiler coal) each week merely to keep the water from rising further. A permanent winding engine, by Andrew Barclay of Kilmarnock (cylinders 22in x 54in) had been installed on this shaft in 1911.

It was suggested that the south shaft be sunk to reach the coal and be used for coal winding until the north shaft could be put into working order. It was estimated that it would take two years to finish the south shaft and cost £26,865 to get the colliery as a whole into working order.

World War I then intervened. A German firm was in the process of constructing the colliery chimney and the war caused an abrupt cessation of work. The half-completed chimney, which bore the date '1914' in white bricks, was eventually completed by an English firm. Regular coal winding began in 1917, though some coal had been worked as early as January 1912.[15] Because of the water, the lower part of the north shaft was abandoned and blocked off at a depth of 750ft, two pumps being installed to keep the water level below the landing; the second shaft was never deepened beyond 750ft. Two seams of the Pensford Series, No 2 and No 3, formed the mainstay of the pit.

The colliery was sunk by Pensford & Bromley Collieries Ltd, formed in December 1909. Because of the great expense of the sinking and difficulties arising from World War I, the company worked at a loss after 1918. A new company, Pensford & Bromley Collieries (1921) Ltd, was registered on 5 February

1921 with a capital of £200,000 to buy the old company, as from 17 May 1921, for £199,356. The valuation was by E. B. Wain of the Chatterley-Whitfield collieries in Staffordshire. The old lease was surrendered and a new one taken out, the landowner accepting only half the usual royalty for the first ten years. Directors of the new company were H. N. Cooper, R. L. James, Egbert Spear (of Dunkerton Colliery), Thomas Wilton and Sir Thomas Wilton, Kt.[16]

To carry away the coal an incline was built to connect the colliery to the GWR line just south of Pensford Viaduct. An agreement was signed on 9 September 1910 under which a self-acting incline, terminating right at the pithead, was proposed. Because this layout would make working difficult, amended plans were proposed on 15 March 1911 whereby the incline would be longer but less steep. The incline was constructed to these plans and was at work in 1912. The sidings at the foot of the incline were laid out so as to enable wagons to be worked by gravity. Certain modifications were made to the layout under an agreement dated 7 June 1919.

The working of the incline remained essentially similar throughout its life. There was a steam hauling engine situated at the head which, in normal operation, would let down a full wagon and haul up an empty one. There was a trap point, which had to be held over when a wagon approached, to divert any runaway wagon before it could do too much damage. Ascending empty wagons, on arrival at the head of the incline, were run back into the colliery sidings while still attached to the rope. Although the incline had a potential capacity of eight wagons per hour, the normal daily traffic was thirty.

In connection with this, the tale is told of the company's efforts to keep a check on the work of their employees by time sheets on which each hour's work had to be entered. One day, the regular engineman on the incline was absent and was replaced by his deputy, who was duly instructed as to the method of filling in his sheet. In the first hour he recorded the despatch of eight loaded wagons but unfortunately forgot to make any further entries until the end of his eight-hour shift when, realising his omission, he hopefully entered the hand-

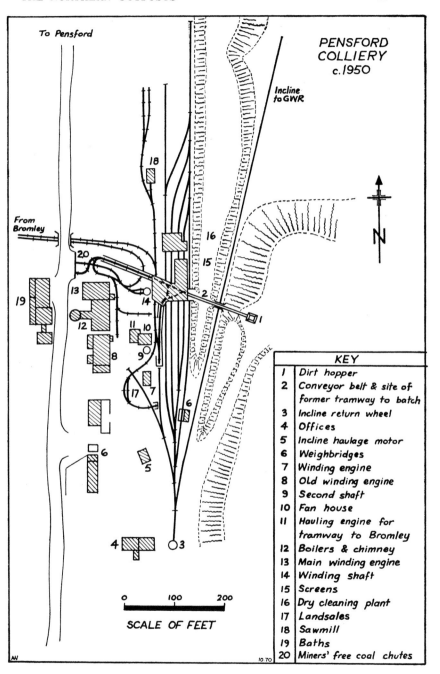

To Pensford

PENSFORD
COLLIERY
c.1950

Incline
to GWR

From
Bromley

N

	KEY
1	Dirt hopper
2	Conveyor belt & site of former tramway to batch
3	Incline return wheel
4	Offices
5	Incline haulage motor
6	Weighbridges
7	Winding engine
8	Old winding engine
9	Second shaft
10	Fan house
11	Hauling engine for tramway to Bromley
12	Boilers & chimney
13	Main winding engine
14	Winding shaft
15	Screens
16	Dry cleaning plant
17	Landsales
18	Sawmill
19	Baths
20	Miners' free coal chutes

0   100   200

SCALE OF FEET

10.70

ling of eight loaded wagons for each of the forgotten hours. The management was at first delighted to find that sixty-four wagons had been despatched but quickly realised that such a figure was impossible. It is said that the subsequent confusion led to the abandonment of time sheets altogether!

Even after the new company was formed, its financial state was uncertain. Between 1921 and 1947, profits totalled £97,762 as against losses of £34,015; it was not until after 1939, however, that profits were regularly made, the years 1932-9 having all shown losses.[17] In February 1922 the men accepted a temporary wage reduction to prevent the pit from closing but, despite this, all employees were given notice of closure in April.[18] The owners agreed to keep the pit open if the men would work below the district minimum wages, and the men went on strike. Eight men remained on duty, firing the five Lancashire boilers that provided steam, and the pit did not reopen until August. In 1929 the company decided to install pithead baths for the men, to try and prevent the drift to other pits,[19] though a ballot of the men showed, surprisingly, only a small majority in favour. The baths, the first in Somerset, were opened in 1931 and, by the following year, the men were said to be very satisfied with them.[20]

Development work was hampered by underground conditions and lack of capital. Nonetheless, despite severe labour shortages, the labour force of 270-330 men could produce about 1,500 tons of coal per week. Output was nearly 140,000 tons in 1930 but there was a progressive decline until, in 1946, only 84,849 tons were produced. This was not significantly improved upon after nationalisation.

Around 1930, Pensford became one of the first Somerset pits regularly to use coal cutters.[21] These not only created a good deal of dust, making working conditions very unpleasant, but also produced a lot of rubbish. Up to forty tubs of dirt per shift had to be wound as a result. This rubbish was at first trammed by hand over bridges across the sidings and incline, to be tipped between the latter and the GWR. Later, ponies were used to pull the tubs and in the 1940s the dirt was tipped into a small road dumper that operated on the tip. Under the

NCB, a conveyor belt was installed to feed dirt to the dumper.

Further modernisation was begun in 1935 with the building of a washery for small coal and the construction of a new electric power plant to provide additional electricity for exploration intended to open out the Bromley No 4 and No 5 seams. These would have been reached by the shaft if it could have been completed, and several attempts were made in the late 1920s to pump out the shaft and reach the Bromley seams that way. Each time, however, the water proved too much, and the new plan was to drive a crossmeasure drift down to cut the seams. Work began in 1936 but the drift struck a large feeder of water and driving had to cease. During 1937 a second drift was driven to try to seal the feeders from the rear but, though it was hoped to complete the work in a year, it was not until 1939 that the coal was reached. Even then, the conditions were far from satisfactory. Fair progress was made during 1940 in opening out the seams but further difficulties were encountered and cementation techniques were resorted to in an effort to control the water. This was successful and in 1946 it was reported that the seams were ready to be worked and should prove to be of great benefit to the National Coal Board. Nationalisation was just round the corner and it is ironic that the company had spent ten years on this development only to be denied the benefit of it. After nationalisation the company was wound up—on 16 March 1955.[22]

The NCB inherited what was the second largest colliery in Somerset but one which was in need of modernisation. Coal was raised in 10-12cwt tubs, two per deck of the single deck cages, which were run up to the screens on a creeper, tipped and run back to the shaft by a creeper and gravity. These screens also dealt with Bromley coal, which arrived on the tramway. The tubs were tipped separately, coal being carried to the screens on a short conveyor belt, and remarshalled into sets for the run back to Bromley.

For many years, Pensford was the only pit in Somerset with any form of coal-washing plant, there being both dry cleaning and contrast washing types at the pithead. After 1 October 1953 Pensford coal was sent to the washery at Old Mills Colliery and the Pensford plant thereafter fell into disuse.

Only two serious mishaps are known to have occurred at the pit. The first was on 2 August 1944 when a cage crashed into the bottom landing, injuring six men. It was found that, because of the wartime blackout, the light on the shaft indicator —which informs the engineman whereabouts the cage is in the shaft—had been removed and used to provide light at the pit top. The overwinding gear had also been unofficially disconnected. The second accident, if it can be so termed, took place in December 1946 when the dirt tip slipped and buried the GWR line, which was not reopened until March 1947.

The NCB prepared a modernisation plan for Pensford but unfortunately the geology was such that mechanisation in the modern style could not be applied. Owing to the rise and fall of the seams due to faulting, many haulage engines and pumps were needed underground, thus making the pit expensive to work. It was for this reason that, in November 1958, the decision was taken to close the pit and the last coal was wound on 13 December of that year. In November, the labour force of 328 men had been halved and, four days after closure, only about sixty men remained for salvage work. This lasted until August 1959, all brick structures being left intact.

The various siding agreements with the GWR were terminated by British Railways on 9 July 1959, after which the rails were removed. Shortly afterwards, the colliery site was taken by Briscon, a firm making prestressed concrete structures. Many of the old buildings were taken over, including the winding-engine houses, and fitters' and carpenters' shops. The steel pithead gear had been demolished before this but the brick building over the south shaft remains intact. It is said that it has been the subject of a preservation order, but this cannot be verified. The sites of both shafts are clearly visible, as is the miners' free coal tip where 2ft gauge rails set in concrete can be seen. Across the road, the pithead baths have found a new use as a sand store. The colliery chimney, once a landmark for miles around, was felled by Dawsons of Clutton soon after closure. Generally, despite the demolition by the new occupants, the major features of the colliery can be found.

RYDON'S (OR RIDING'S) COLLIERY

This little pit was one of several in the area of Stanton Drew. Sinking of two shafts began on 25 March 1808 on land leased from the Tornewell Estate by Messrs Fowler, Player, Cox and Rogers. Mr Fowler had pits in Coalpit Lane nearby which, in 1824, had ceased working.[23] The coaling shaft was served by a condensing winding engine of 10hp while the pumping shaft had a 28hp engine.

George Rogers (if George was his Christian name) was also the bailiff but lacked the experience needed for the job and the working of the pit suffered as a result. When Cox and Fowler died, their shares passed to their families, who were too poor to put up the fresh capital that was so urgently required.

The coaling pit was sunk just outside the outcrop of the Hard Vein and the water pit was 41ft away. At a depth between 60ft and 108ft the coaling shaft met the Gore Vein and from there a level was driven for 490ft to a brook at Low Close. It is highly probable that the duty of the pumping engine was to raise water from the sump to this level, whence it could drain by gravity.

Stutchbury says that the pit was worked to the worst possible system, but neither this nor the lack of capital caused the closure. In 1832 or 1833 an inrush of water in the Little Vein flooded the workings and the pit was abandoned.

FARMBOROUGH COLLIERY[24]

The story of Farmborough Colliery is one of spectacular failure, parallelled in Somerset possibly only by the sinking at Buckland Dinham, which had many similarities with Farmborough. The names of the initial proprietors at Farmborough are unknown though a George Payne is thought to have been involved, but two years after the sinking of the first shaft began, Charles Hollwey assumed control. Sinking of this shaft began in March 1840 on the outskirts of Farmborough village, a mile north of the Timsbury pits. The site was chosen on the assumption that the Timsbury coal would be met with at Farmborough, but this hypothesis did not take into account the Farmborough Fault, which separates the two areas.

The first 42ft of ground were faulty and delayed the work somewhat but, at the beginning of 1841, a depth of 180ft had been reached. Here sinking stopped for a year due to a delay in the delivery of the winding and pumping engines. At 195ft, water began to be encountered, the flow being 8,500gph. To try to control this, sinking of the No 2 shaft was begun in February 1842 and, when this reached the water on 18 June 1842, a flow of 7,380gph was encountered in it.

The first coal, a seam 9in thick, was found early in 1843 at a depth of 300ft, a discovery that must have given the adventurers some heart after three years of fruitless work. In August 1843 a branch was put through to No 2 pit, then 330ft deep, in a seam of coal 13in thick. The No 1 shaft was then at 540ft. Thus far, things were fairly promising, though the coal discovered was not particularly significant.

Difficulties were now met with, for on 20 January 1844, at a depth of 480ft, the sinking of the No 2 pit ceased, due to an inrush of water, and was not resumed until 14 October of that year. No 1 pit had apparently missed this inrush and, at a depth of 870ft, had proved another four seams of thin coal. However, work on this shaft was stopped in December 1844 with a water flow of 210gph and did not resume until 18 August of the following year, after which the water flow progressively decreased. No 2 shaft had also stopped in December 1844 when a large flow of water (2,390gph) made further sinking impossible until 29 March 1845, on which date the pit was at 498ft.

The financial state of the undertaking, which after an immense outlay over a period of five years had produced no worthwhile result, may well be imagined, and it says much for the tenacity—and perhaps the foolhardiness—of the adventurers that the sinkings were continued. Eventually though, at a depth of 840ft, the No 2 shaft was stopped. All effort was then concentrated on the No 1 shaft which, by June 1846, had reached 1,164ft.

Five branches were put out from the shaft as the sinking progressed, but these proved only faulted ground and no coal was seen. On 3 August 1846 another coal seam, only $2\frac{1}{4}$in thick, was proved and with this disappointing discovery the proprietors lost heart. At the end of March 1847, at a depth of 1,413ft, the sinking was terminated and in a last desperate attempt a borehole was put down from shaft bottom to a depth of 1,440ft. Nothing was found.

With this, the venture was abandoned. A large quantity of new plant—engines, rails and wagons—was left on site, and in 1849 the collection was inspected by the Timsbury proprietors with a view to buying it for their new pit at Lower Conygre; but the acquisition was not proceeded with and the final disposal of the plant remains unknown. Little is to be seen today other than the dirt tips, but the memories have survived longer than the material. The recollections of the enterprise, the endeavour and the final failure are, even today, strong in the village and the coalfield.

COMMON WOOD LEVEL

This venture represents the most recent proposal for reviving coalmining in Somerset. First rumours of a new mine reached the authors' ears in October 1967, but it was not until June 1969 that work actually began on a site near Hunstrete, Marksbury.

The work undertaken to date has been entirely exploratory, testing the ground before obtaining a licence from the NCB to open a private colliery. To date, the licence has not been taken. The proposal for the colliery is in the hands of Gasex (Mining Engineers) Ltd, which company was formed on 31 May 1967 to take over Gasex of Warminster as a going concern. The nominal capital of the enterprise is £2,000 and the directors are Mr and Mrs A. Hann and K. A. I. Pearce.[25]

Planning permission has been granted for an initial seven-year period subject to the conditions that no spoil tips would be made and that a maximum of thirty men would work at the site. Results of the explorations have not been very encouraging. One trial level has drawn a blank while another had, by August 1969, proved coal thought to be equivalent to the Slyving seam of the Radstock Series. However, unsuspected workings dating back to the mid-1700s have been found to make the working of coal an economic impossibility.

In October 1969 all work ceased for the winter. The decision was subsequently taken to cease exploration at that particular location and the temporary 2ft gauge railway and tubs, together with other equipment, have been disposed of. It is possible that work may restart at a nearby site in 1971, though the decision to do this has yet to be made.

To conclude, we may mention the fate of a much earlier venture at Hunstrete. On 18 March 1829 Messrs Langford, Hill & James took out leases of coal in the area. In a letter dated 11 May 1832, James stated that 'we despair of finding Coal at Hound Street' and that, due to the difficult strata, it was wished to abandon the entire venture.[26] It is to be hoped that the Gasex venture will have more success.

Notes begin on page 266.

4 THE EARL OF WARWICK'S CLUTTON COLLIERIES

The Earl of Warwick's estates in Somerset included nearly all the parish of Clutton and possessed sawmills, quarries, brick-works and collieries as adjuncts to their agricultural basis. The early coal workings were of the shallow bell pit type; Collinson in 1791 commented: 'the country abounds with excellent coals' and the coal was often so heavily coated in sulphur 'that in all its joints it seemed to be covered with leaf gold'. There were two important collieries—Frys Bottom and Greyfield—together with the smaller mines at Mooresland, Rudges, Knapp Hill and Burchells.

FRYS BOTTOM

This pit was at work by 1838, in which year it was occupied by James Rossiter & Co.[1] On 6 May 1863 an agreement was made between the Earl of Warwick and the promoters of the B & NSR allowing the latter to construct a siding from Clutton Station for $\frac{3}{4}$ mile to the colliery. It was stipulated that the siding should form only one junction with the main line and should be completed within twelve months of the opening of the railway. This last event took place on 3 September 1873. At a later date, the siding into Burchells Colliery was connected to the Frys Bottom line some 200yd north of Clutton Station.

Coal was at first wound in hudges, a horse gin providing the power, but this system was superseded by a winding engine supplied with steam by a 'Haycock' type of boiler. In March 1862 an old $4\frac{1}{2}$ ton boiler was sold for scrap, which may have been the 'Haycock'.[2] The headgear was wooden, supporting a

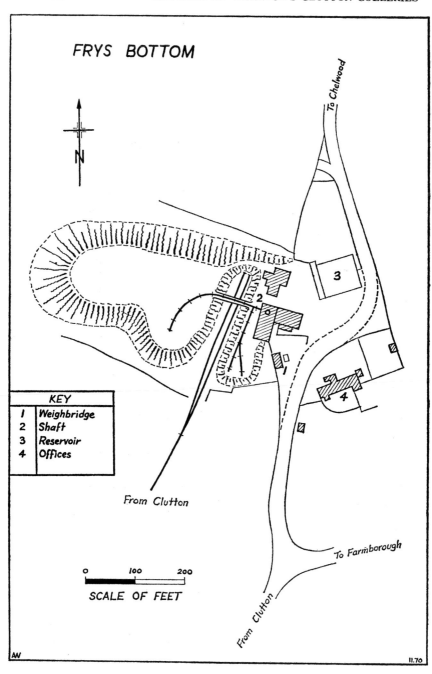

FRYS BOTTOM

To Chelwood

3

2

1

4

KEY

1	Weighbridge
2	Shaft
3	Reservoir
4	Offices

From Clutton

To Farmborough

From Clutton

0   100   200

SCALE OF FEET

AW

11.70

single pulley over which passed the flat winding rope. Only one accident is known to have occurred at the pit: on 8 July 1867 two men were drowned when water from old workings flooded into the colliery.

In the 1880s one Robert Owen is recorded as going to work in the pit at the age of nine. The men worked until late at night and his mother had to come and fetch him since he was afraid to walk home in the dark! At the same period, when the men were paid on Saturday nights, they would return home via the Hunter's Rest Inn at Chelwood where beer then cost $1\frac{1}{2}$d per pint. The beer was put out on the wall in bath tubs for the miners to dip their own mugs into.

The men once petitioned for closure of the colliery, though the reason for this has not been recorded. However, after being suspended since 1887,[3] the pit was shut permanently on 31 July 1895.[4] The headgear was demolished and, two years later, the chimney was felled, a J. H. Cook being injured by the falling masonry. At the colliery there remains the derelict weighbridge office and one of the capped shafts, while the track bed of the siding is clear for its entire length. An iron girder bridge carrying the line over a farm track at Clutton bears the legend 'W. EVANS PAULTON 1871'.

GREYFIELD[5]
Greyfield had its beginnings in an indenture of 9 March 1833 by which the Earl of Warwick leased minerals to John Savage Cameron, together with the right to sink a pit. The term was $40\frac{1}{2}$ years and the Earl was to receive either a tenth of the coal raised from the pit or money to that value .

A document of 12 March 1833 laid down the shares in the pit:

John Cameron	4/8	Samuel Foster	1/8
David Cooke	2/8	Earl of Warwick	1/8

At the same time it was reported that engines, works, buildings, machinery, horses' etc had been set up.

Cameron died on 18 October 1833 and left his shares in the colliery to his nephew, Alexander Cameron Ford. Six years later, John and William Rees-Mogg each acquired an eighth share from Ford and, on 8 May 1843, they obtained half of Cooke's shares as well; thus, by this date, they controlled half the shares in the pit.

A deed of 11 February 1842 stated that

> large sums [have] been from time to time expended in and about the said colliery and a new 90hp Engine has been erected but the shaft . . . has not been sunk to the Bottom vein and the . . . pumps and working pieces have not been completely constructed and a considerable time will elapse before such works will be completed . . .[6]

The large sums referred to included £5,250 for the engine, shafts and pumps; as soon as the shaft had been completed, a call of £1,000 per share was to be made. At this period the pit was trading under the title of the Greyfield Coal Co.

Because of the capital required to complete the works, Ford and Cooke were unable to pay the necessarily large calls upon their shares and these were defrayed by the Earl of Warwick, Samuel Foster and the Rees-Moggs; as a result the two unfortunate partners became liable for gradually increasing debts. Foster's share was purchased by the Rees-Moggs in 1855.

On 15 July 1848 Charles Hollwey was admitted as a partner, and the shares then stood as follows:

Alexander Ford	2/9	Earl of Warwick	1/9
Samuel Foster	1/9	Charles Hollwey	1/9

The Rees-Moggs held the remaining four-ninths, one-ninth each of their own and two-ninths as trustees of David Cooke. In addition to becoming a partner, Hollwey was appointed manager of the colliery at £100pa.

The pit went through a bad time in 1858: Hollwey wrote that 'the underground workings are very dismaying and the Trade with the exception of the Gas Contract is scarcely worth mention'. Trade was still slack three years later, the first quarter of 1861 showing an income of £529 against an expenditure (excluding wages) of less than £200. Coke was being produced at this time; the Farrington Coal Co purchased 6s worth of it, although the weight is not mentioned.

We can now turn to the physical details of the colliery. There were two winding shafts, but these were not contemporary sinkings; the older (nearer the winding engine) was

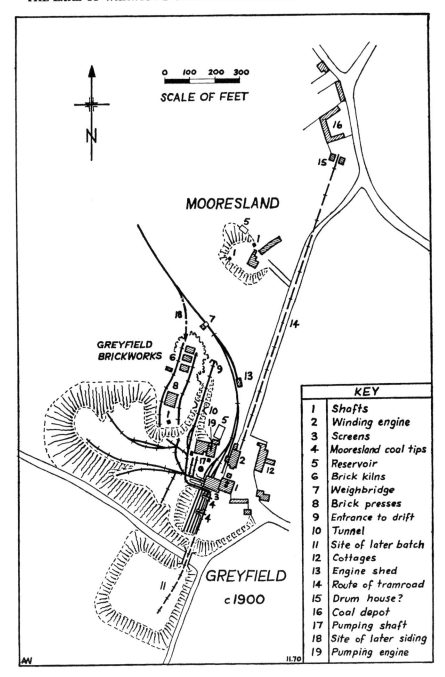

SCALE OF FEET

N

MOORESLAND

GREYFIELD
BRICKWORKS

GREYFIELD
c 1900

KEY		
	1	Shafts
	2	Winding engine
	3	Screens
	4	Mooresland coal tips
	5	Reservoir
	6	Brick kilns
	7	Weighbridge
	8	Brick presses
	9	Entrance to drift
	10	Tunnel
	11	Site of later batch
	12	Cottages
	13	Engine shed
	14	Route of tramroad
	15	Drum house?
	16	Coal depot
	17	Pumping shaft
	18	Site of later siding
	19	Pumping engine

square with wooden guides, while the other was 10ft in diameter and had wire rope guides. The second shaft may have been sunk when cages were introduced in the 1860s.[7] Manriding was often rather hazardous; the story is told of a Mr Brimble who once fell out of the cage in the older shaft. Fortunately he lodged in a recess and the men in the next cage to pass were rather disconcerted to hear a voice in the darkness calling for some light!

A third shaft, used solely for ventilation, lay to the north of the coaling shafts. The fourth shaft was equipped with a Cornish beam engine for pumping water from the workings; this engine was completely overhauled in April 1864 at a cost of £350.[8]

In addition to the shafts there was a drift running northeast from a point near the ventilation shaft. Known as 'the Cuckoo' (a nickname for one of the coal seams), this drift led to the bottom of the shafts at Mooresland Colliery, a few hundred yards from Greyfield. Originally Mooresland had led an independent existence, being sunk to the Radstock Series some time after 1840; at an unknown date, the output was transferred to Greyfield via the drift and a narrow gauge tramway, and thereafter its shafts were only used for ventilation.

The coaling shafts were wound by a steam engine, as were many of the underground inclines. These hauling engines were repaired at Paulton Foundry during the 1860s, a new engine being delivered in September 1861 for £254. In later days, electric hauling engines were also used underground. Output during the year to 23 May 1846 was 11,900 tons, which in 1889 had increased to about 60,000 tons, no doubt as a result of the extensive modernisation carried out over the intervening years. Thus, by the late nineteenth century, Greyfield was one of the most important collieries in Somerset.

At first, owing to the lack of any road access to the pithead, a double track tramroad incline, with a drum (and presumably a hauling engine) at its head, was built from the colliery up to a coal depot on the Bath to High Littleton road. This tramroad did not survive for very long; a map of 1836 shows a road down to the pit,[9] partly on the course of the tramroad, but the tithe map of 1838 shows the tramroad but no road!

In 1847 a broad gauge railway was proposed to serve the colliery but the proposal came to nothing and it was not until 1873 that a siding was laid off the B & NSR, under the same agreement by which the Frys Bottom line was laid. Apart from the colliery sidings, the siding was the responsibility of the GWR. At the pithead, narrow-gauge lines spanned the sidings to reach the dirt tips, and also served the Cuckoo drift and the colliery brickworks.

At first the siding appears to have been worked by horses, which pulled up the empty trucks, the loads being allowed to run down to the GWR by gravity. The first locomotive was an 0-4-0 saddle tank built by R. W. Hawthorn in 1885; it was painted black and bore the name *Francis,* though it was familiarly known as *The Coffee Pot.*[10] Gravity working must have ceased after the arrival of this locomotive, except for a period in 1894 when the engine was under repair. On 10 January a train of wagons being run down got out of control on icy rails and eight wagons were 'smashed to splinters' at the GWR sidings.

In 1894 a new locomotive arrived. Named *Daisy,* it was an 0-4-0 saddle tank built by Pecketts of Bristol. *Francis* lay derelict by the engine shed for a few years before being scrapped. When *Daisy* was out of order once, another locomotive named *Emlyn* was borrowed from C. D. Phillips of Newport. This firm hired out many locomotives named *Emlyn* so the identity of the Greyfield engine cannot be ascertained. *Daisy* was returned to her maker in 1904 for a new steel boiler, and another new boiler was fitted in December 1916, at which date the engine was working at Burchells Colliery.[11]

On 4 June 1904 the Cuckoo drift and the Mooresland workings were abandoned. Around 1906 the GWR agreed to construct a junction for a siding to serve the brickworks: though it was duly completed, the siding did not see much use, since the brickworks closed about 1909.

On 14 September of that year the colliery was the scene of a major disaster when water from old workings broke into the Streak Vein. There was no loss of life, fortunately, because the

main inrush of water was carried away into the lowest workings of the New Vein, where no men were at work; and the
miners, including two who were temporarily trapped, were
able to reach the shaft in safety. The only casualties in fact
were six pit ponies, drowned in the Dabchick Vein.

By 30 September 1909 the pit had been cleared of water and
most men were back at work. However, on 31 December 1909
some men were given notice due to the closing of one district;
and on 28 May 1911, 152 men and boys were made redundant
by the closure of the whole colliery following royalty difficulties.[12]

In the ironic words of the Clutton schoolmaster, it was 'a
black day for the village'. For a few months machinery was
salvaged; the hauling engine in the Dabchick Vein was
brought to the surface on 16 June 1911, while that from the
New Vein was sent to Burchells Colliery for further use. On
21 November, J. H. and F. W. Cook cut the cage guides at the
bottom of the pit and the shaft was used for the last time.[13]

Today there are several important remains of the colliery.
The earthworks of the siding are traceable right up to the pit,
where the major surviving structure is the winding engine
house, now a dwelling house. The heapstead, locomotive shed
and a tunnel carrying a footpath under the sidings can also be
seen, as can the entrance to the Cuckoo drift. Otherwise the
new buildings of a transport company have obliterated most
features. At Mooresland Colliery only the dirt tip remains,
while one or two stone sleeper blocks can be found on the
route of the old incline up to the coal depot, of which no trace
remains.

CLUTTON OR BURCHELLS

Before the flood at Greyfield in 1909 it was becoming increasingly apparent to its owners that the pit was nearing the
end of its useful life, and preparations were made to open a
new colliery near Clutton Station. Towards the end of 1908
the Clutton Coal Co, a subsidiary of the Greyfield Colliery Co
Ltd, was formed and work began at two sites. A few hundred
yards north of Clutton Station lay an old shaft which was re-

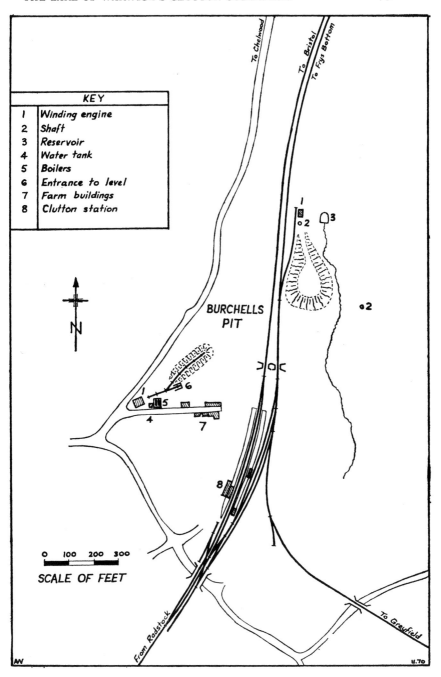

KEY

1	Winding engine
2	Shaft
3	Reservoir
4	Water tank
5	Boilers
6	Entrance to level
7	Farm buildings
8	Clutton station

BURCHELLS PIT

To Chelwood

To Bristol

To Frys Bottom

N

SCALE OF FEET

0 100 200 300

From Radstock

To Greyfield

opened as a coal winding shaft. At the same time a new drift was begun, to the west of the GWR and following the inclination of the seams down under the railway towards the bottom of the refurbished shaft. The drift was under construction in June 1909 and probably began work in 1910.

At first, some of the equipment for the new colliery—boilers, stationary engines, etc—came from Joseph Pugsley of Bristol but when Greyfield closed in 1911 much of the machinery was transferred to Clutton to replace that obtained from Pugsley. The men from Greyfield were also transferred *en bloc* and by March 1912 there were nearly 350 employees.[14]

The drift provided coal for landsale and also served for access to the workings. A single track tramway of about 2ft 6in gauge emerged from the drift, sets of eight or nine tubs being hauled out by an engine situated at the head of the incline. The shaft was served by a standard gauge siding off the Frys Bottom line, wagons being shunted by *Daisy* from Greyfield. North of the winding engine house here were the boilers and chimney as well as an air compressor and sawmill. The chimney, and that at the drift, was built 60ft high by Dawsons of Clutton, with provision for extension to 100ft should this be required.

First rumours of closure came in September 1918, when the Coal Controller said that it was intended to close the pit 'in the near future' and that the men would have to move to other collieries in the area. This invoked a strong reaction from the Somerset Miners' Association who gained the concession that there would be no interference with the pit so long as it maintained its existing output of 780 tons per week.[15]

On 27 April 1920 the pit was partially closed through an inrush of water from the flooded Greyfield workings.[16] The existing pumps were inadequate and the pit thereafter worked only the coal above the water.

The end came in 1921. On 21 March the owners made it known that they intended to close the pit at the end of the month. Burchells was still at work in April but at the beginning of May a very disheartening statement was issued. This said that the company was in a very bad financial position and that coal reserves were almost exhausted; in fact, there was not even enough coal to keep the colliery boilers in steam. Throughout the 1921 lockout, the Clutton men remained at work, defying their union, for wages far below the minimum agreed district rates.[17]

Most mining ceased on 25 August and on 29 August H. Godfrey Peyton (secretary to the Greyfield company) announced that there was no alternative to closure and that he had already given instructions for dismantling to begin. The men responded by offering to take whatever wages the pit would pay; the company agreed but the SMA refused to allow it and the men were forced to agree with their union.

Lady Warwick then entered the discussions, expressing sorrow at the closure and saying that she would have liked the colliery to continue to work as a co-operative enterprise. This announcement came too late; dismantling had already begun, the pumps had been removed and the rails, other than those on the main inclines, had been dismantled. In October 1921 a company was being formed to reopen the pit but nothing came of this.

Underground salvage had ceased by 11 October and *Daisy* had been returned to Pecketts for rebuilding and resale, but otherwise the machinery was intact. It lay at Clutton for about three years, earmarked for a new drift at Cloud Hill which never came into being, and was eventually sold for scrap after 1924. A small brickworks was established by the site of the shaft but this failed and was closed soon after 1929.

At the drift, only a stable remains today, while, by the railway, the chimney is the most obvious relic. The site has been much interfered with and, apart from the conifer-planted batch, few features can be discerned with certainty.

KNAPP HILL

Managed by J. W. Cottle, this small drift mine is believed to have been opened after the 1921 strike. The haulage drift emerged behind the tips at Burchells Colliery; it is not known whether Knapp Hill coal was ever loaded at the railway siding. The mine was abandoned about 16 March 1923 and only the traces of the haulage drift still survive.[18]

THE PROPOSED CLOUD HILL COLLIERY[19]

As we have seen, the attempts to restart Burchells as a co-operative enterprise were a failure. Nonetheless, in April 1923 a new mine was proposed, to be run under similar principles. The scheme was to work the Rudge seam in areas missed by Knapp Hill and the old Rudges Pit; this latter, sunk in 1847 and closed about 1854, had achieved an output of less than 90 tons per week and worked less than 20 acres of coal. Exploration in 1918, on which these new proposals were based, had suggested that, at least at its outcrops, the Rudge was of good quality.

With a capital of £17,000 it was intended to lease 200 acres of coal south of Clutton and drive a pair of drifts down to the seam, using one of the two Rudges Pit shafts for ventilation. From the drifts, a tramway would be laid across the fields to Cloud Hill quarry, which was served by an existing siding off the GWR.

A large amount of surplus plant at Knapp Hill, Burchells and Greyfield was earmarked for the new venture, but it is hardly surprising that the latter failed before it began. Even if mining had been started, the optimism regarding the Rudge seam would probably have proved to be ill-founded, as was later the case at Marsh Lane Colliery.

Notes begin on page 266.

5 PAULTON BASIN

If one stands and surveys the desolation and ruins of Paulton basin, erstwhile terminus of the northern branch of the SCC, it is almost impossible to visualise the hive of industry that it must have been in its heyday. The bed of the canal is now but a marsh, many of the buildings have vanished, and everywhere there are weeds, crumbling stonework and dereliction. However, Paulton basin was once served by no less than five tramroads, linking at least fifteen collieries to the canal. Most of these collieries have been closed for upwards of 100 years and information is often hard to come by. In this chapter, we consider the tramroads first (except those at Withy Mills and Radford, which are dealt with separately), then the history of the pits they served.

TRAMROADS

The routes of these can be seen on the maps; information about their construction has been published elsewhere, notably in Kenneth Clew's *The Somersetshire Coal Canal and Railways,* so only brief details are given here.

On the northern side of Paulton Basin was the terminus for the tramroad that served Old Grove, Prior's, Tyning and Hayeswood pits. From this line a lengthy branch diverged to Amesbury and Mearns pits, but this branch probably saw relatively little use. As far as Old Grove, however, the line was still at work in 1873.[1] Both these tramroads were laid with edge rails on stone sleeper blocks and were probably entirely horseworked.

To the south of the basin the three tramroads were laid

with 'L' plates, again on stone blocks. Two short tramroads served Paulton Foundry and adjacent collieries but the main line ran up the hill to the Brittens pits (probably on a self-acting incline) and thence via Littlebrook, Paulton Ham, Paulton Hill and Simons Hill pits to terminate in the yard of Salisbury Colliery. The entire line was disused by 1871, as were the collieries it served.

The routes of the tramroads are easily traceable except for the Mearns and Amesbury line. Stone sleeper blocks can be seen at many points, sometimes in situ and sometimes lying in hedgerows. Excavations have revealed blocks and tramplates in position at Brittens and Paulton Basin, while blocks alone have been dug up at numerous other locations.

PROJECTED TRAMROADS
The SCC-deposited plans of 1793 show tramroad extensions off the Mearns line to serve five other pits. There is no evidence that any of these were built, but it is possible that the line to Woody Heighgrove Colliery was constructed and used for a short time.

SALISBURY COLLIERY
In 1820 the pit was owned by William Rawlins. It had been opened about 1792 and was closed by 1873 (probably in the 1840s). The remains of the batch near Salisbury Farm are the only traces today.

SIMONS HILL COLLIERY
Variously known as Simons or Simmons Hill this pit was at work in 1791, when coal was sold at 4d per bushel. In 1824, a pit on the hill east of Paulton was said to have been worked between 1790 and 1800 by Simon Hill. By 1840, it was owned by the Rev James Rawlings and others. 'Haycock' boilers were used to provide steam, one once exploding. The pit was closed about 1844 and only the tip and capped shaft remain today.

PAULTON HILL COLLIERY
In the early 1840s this pit was owned by a Mr Hill, possibly

Page 85 (above) The pithead at Upper Conygre Colliery. Note the single pulley wheel and loaded coal carts; (below) GWR locomotive shunting wagons at Camerton Colliery in about 1910

Page 86 (above) A busy scene at Dunkerton Colliery c 1920;
(below) Farrington Colliery viewed from the approach road

the Simon Hill mentioned above, and has often been confused with Simons Hill Colliery. The pit was closed by 1864 and only the dirt tip remains.

PAULTON HAM COLLIERY
In the early 1840s the pit was owned by a Mr Randall and was still at work in 1855; it had closed by 1864.

LITTLEBROOK COLLIERY
This pit had two shafts, and is supposed to have been connected underground to Crossways and Brittens pits. It was closed in the 1850s. Apart from the dirt tip, no trace remains today.

CROSSWAYS PIT
Located near Brittens crossroads (hence the name) the pit had a 5ft diameter shaft and was 144ft deep.

BRITTENS LOWER PIT
No information about this pit exists; it had been closed by 1864 and only the small batch remains, at the rear of Brittens Farm.

BRITTENS NEW PIT
Closed by 1864, faint traces of the batch remain near the Somerset Inn. The shaft, according to NCB records, is under the inn.

PAULTON BRASS & IRON FOUNDRY
This was established by 1810 by Joseph Hill, Thomas Randall and William Rawlins, who had then 'set up and completed several foundries . . . for the establishing and completely carrying on and prosecuting the business of an Iron Founder on a very large and expensive scale.'

The land was held in trust by Richard Langford for a term of 89 years to 1899.[2] By 7 February 1839, the foundry was occupied by William Evans and the Paulton Coal Co. It was still at work in 1869 and probably at least up to 1889; it may

F

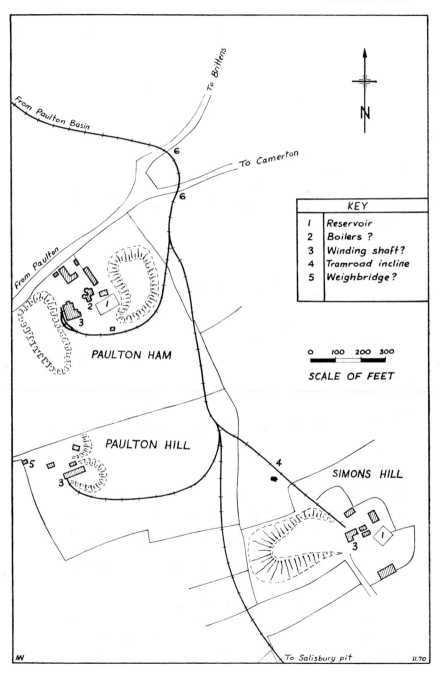

still have been at work in 1895, but closed shortly afterwards. In 1887 and 1889 auctions of the surrounding lands were held, the foundry workshops being sold in the latter year. These auctions probably indicate that the foundry was then more or less disused.

Paulton Foundry, the only major foundry in the coalfield, played an important part in the growth of mining. Winding and pumping engines were built there, together with all the other items needed for a coalmine. Articles of a more mundane nature—grates and kitchen stoves—were also built to order. One of the foundry's winding engines is now preserved for the Bristol City Museum, but the most lasting products were the massive cast-iron gateposts which survive in abundance, defying both removal and decay. It is rumoured that Evans perfected a process for making non-rusting iron, which involved pouring oil into the mould as the molten metal solidified; hence the longevity of some of the products. Soon after Paulton Foundry closed, the business moved to a site beside Lower Writhlington Colliery; after the 1940s the foundry was again transferred to Frome Hill in Radstock, where it is still at work. Many of the buildings can be seen at Paulton today, in various stages of deterioration and collapse.

PAULTON ENGINE COLLIERY
Situated beside Paulton Foundry, this is popularly supposed to have been the earliest pit in the area.[3] It is said that the first Newcomen pumping engine in Somerset was erected here in 1750, though some doubt has been cast on this claim.[4] The pit is certainly one of the two in Paulton that in 1791 was worked by 'fire engines' and doubtless took its name from that fact.[5] There were two shafts, one of which was 609ft deep to the Bull vein; the Farrington Series of seams was also proved, by a crossmeasure drift, but not worked to any great extent.

The colliery was the scene of a serious accident on 24 March 1830, when the rope broke and four men and a boy were killed when they fell back down the shaft. In 1839, the pit was owned by the Paulton Coal Co (agent, John Rossiter) who also had part occupation of Paulton Foundry. In 1842 the manager

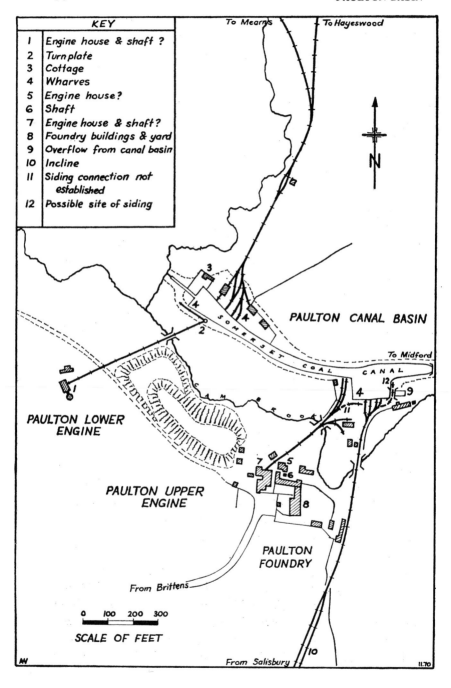

KEY

1	Engine house & shaft ?
2	Turn plate
3	Cottage
4	Wharves
5	Engine house?
6	Shaft
7	Engine house & shaft?
8	Foundry buildings & yard
9	Overflow from canal basin
10	Incline
11	Siding connection not established
12	Possible site of siding

To Mearns
To Hayeswood

PAULTON CANAL BASIN

To Midford

PAULTON LOWER ENGINE

PAULTON UPPER ENGINE

PAULTON FOUNDRY

From Brittens

0   100   200   300
SCALE OF FEET

From Salisbury

11.70

was William Ashman, who designed the locomotive used on the SCC tramroad in 1826; possibly this engine was built in Paulton.

In 1852 the pumping engine was purchased by the Timsbury proprietors for use at Withy Mills Colliery; and possibly a new engine was erected at Paulton. The Paulton Engine Coal Co was working Timsbury coal illegally in 1858, and on 7 June of that year, Mr Evans of Paulton agreed to pay compensation for his ill-gotten gains.[6]

The latest known working date for the colliery is November 1869 and, by 1873, the pit was used only for pumping water from the Timsbury Collieries. On 1 October 1873 Charles Simmons purchased the 'engine house', so possibly even pumping had ceased by then. In April 1889, land including the 'Engine Coalwork' was auctioned and the pit was certainly shut by this date.

Today, little remains other than the dirt tip and one of the shafts. Certain buildings, such as the counting house, were used jointly with the foundry, so it is possible that some of the remaining buildings belonged to the colliery rather than the foundry.

BREWER'S PIT
Owned by a Mr Brewer, in 1700 this pit was using an 8ft diameter waterwheel for pumping, drawing water from a depth of 102ft. The exact location of this shaft is unknown.

GOOSARD PIT
Otherwise known as Gooseward or Goosewardsham Pit or Paulton Lower Engine, it is reputed to have been sunk by two colliers in 1708. No traces remain today, the site now being a sewage works.

PAULTON BOTTOM COLLIERY
Also known as Paulton Lower Colliery, this had two shafts which, covered by concrete caps, can still be seen today.

OLD TYNING COLLIERY
This pit, on land owned by William Savage, was possibly

started in 1766. In 1791-2 a drainage level from Radford Bridge was built to serve this pit and Old Grove at a cost of £1,200. Old Tyning was closed in about 1792, being superceded by New Tyning.

NEW TYNING COLLIERY

On 24 January 1791 the six Timsbury coal proprietors signed articles of a 200-year partnership in connection with their intention to sink two new collieries.[7] The shares were divided as follows:

Jacob Mogg	2/8	Samborne Palmer	1/8
William Crang	1/8	James Savage	1/8
John Crang	1/8	Alexander Adams	1/8 + 1/8

The capital was subscribed according to these shares, except that Palmer was exempt; Adams was only a life partner and may have defrayed Palmer's share.

Coal was to be landed at two pits: the first, New Tyning was to be 'forthwith begun'; while New Grove had to begin within a year. It was specified that when each pit began winding, the partners connected with the old pits of the same names would 'shut up same'. The partners agreed to raise £1,000 to repay the expenses incurred by Mogg, Adams, Savage and J. Crang in making the level to the old pits, which would be altered to serve New Tyning. New Tyning had, in fact, been considered in 1788 but was not proceeded with at the time.[8]

New Tyning was worked by the partnership under the style of Mogg, Parish & Co and had a steam pumping engine from its inception; the order in June 1842 of thirty 'archhead links' suggests that it was of the Newcomen type with a laminated beam.[9] The pit was shut down in October 1856 but remained in use pumping water for Old Grove at least up to 1860.

NEW GROVE COLLIERY

Under the partnership agreement of 24 January 1791 it was agreed that New Grove would be started before 1792, after which Old Grove would be closed. It appears that the funds were insufficient for sinking both New Tyning and New

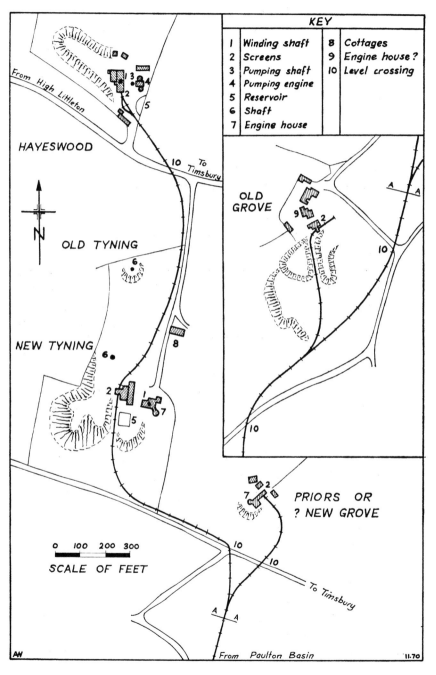

KEY

1	Winding shaft	8	Cottages
2	Screens	9	Engine house ?
3	Pumping shaft	10	Level crossing
4	Pumping engine		
5	Reservoir		
6	Shaft		
7	Engine house		

From High Littleton

HAYESWOOD

To Timsbury

OLD GROVE

N

OLD TYNING

NEW TYNING

PRIORS OR ? NEW GROVE

To Timsbury

0   100   200   300

SCALE OF FEET

From Paulton Basin

11.70

Grove and the latter, after a little preliminary work, was abandoned in favour of modernisation at Old Grove. There is a small batch near Old Grove that may represent the start of the sinking. As a point of interest, the 1791 agreement specified that, when the pit was closed, the shaft was to be filled up and 'sown with Rye Grass seeds'—possibly the earliest example of concern over derelict land!

OLD GROVE COLLIERY

This was begun by Jacob Mogg, Alexander Adams and John Bush on 27 November 1765, when they took a 21-year lease from Edward Popham, lord of the manor of Timsbury.[10] An agreement to start the sinking was signed on 17 January 1766[11] and a shaft of 4ft 6in diameter was sunk through the Radstock Series.

In June 1838 the possibility of sinking the shaft down to the Farrington Series was discussed; and it was estimated that a trial sinking of 600ft would cost £1,000. Savage, Bush and Parish who owned 41/64 of the shares agreed to bear the expense of this. On 5 April 1841 it was further decided to sink the second shaft down to these seams at a cost of £400. Work was completed about 1846 at a depth of 1,373ft, proving five seams. This was the first shaft to pass through both the Radstock and Farrington Series and as such proved to be of great geological interest.

There is little information about the engines. A 26in steam cylinder was supplied in 1863, possibly for the winding engine, while in 1853 and 1861 archhead links were supplied for the pumping engine, which may have been of the Newcomen type. In the 1850s there was a lot of trouble with the winding ropes and about 1857 the flat hemp were replaced by round wire ropes, though not before one of the hemp ropes had snapped and temporarily closed the pit.

By the 1860s, Old Grove was in low water. On 7 May 1860 the pit's lease was offered to Sarle & Co of Seend Ironworks, Devizes, but they declined to take it. They did, however, make a contract for the supply of coal, in return for which Old Grove agreed to purchase 5 tons of iron rails for relaying the tramroad. In 1869, James McMurtrie reported on the pit. In the first half of the year, 2,794 tons of coal had been raised at a cost in wages of 6s 10½d per ton. The proprietors had recently installed a new pumping engine, possibly to cope with water from New Tyning, but McMurtrie's verdict was that there was 'little hope of the colliery as it now stands to be worked at profit'. Nonetheless, a profit of about £100 in January 1870 decided the proprietors to continue working the pit. It was still at work in 1873, but had closed by 1878. There are few remains other than the dirt tip today, but excavations have shown the stone blocks of the tramroad to be still in situ.

PRIOR'S PIT
Although this pit figures in a list of wages for sinkers and branchers drawn up on 22 August 1792, it appears that it was used only for ventilating the water level to Hayeswood Colliery.[12] It is possible that Prior's is an alternative name for New Grove Colliery.[13]

HAYESWOOD COLLIERY
Opened about 1750, the colliery later came under the partnership of Palmer, Mogg, Crang & Co, which was created on 5 March 1792 to work it.[14] Little is known of the colliery until the 1840s. On 3 May 1841 it was decided to erect a new coke

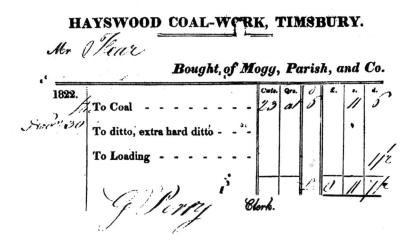

oven at the pit, and four weeks later £600 was allocated to 're establish Hayeswood Coalwork'; this may refer to a temporary closure, or simply to modernisation. On 23 January 1845 there was a serious accident when, due to the inattention of the winding engineman, a hudge carrying seven men was drawn over the wheel and the men injured. Worse was to come: on 4 February 1845, the pit was inundated by an irruption of water from old workings. Nearly 100 men were underground and seven men and four boys were drowned before they could be got out.

As a result the pit was closed, the men and output quota being divided amongst the other collieries. On 10 February, a special meeting of the proprietors recorded

> their great sense of the intrepid and humane conduct of Findlater Crang Esq., . . . in descending and remaining underground and by his energy and example encouraging the men in their attempt to recover the bodies of those who perished . . .

Attempts were made to pump out the water but it was decided that the pit should close on 7 June 1845 and William Evans was asked to value the plant. S. S. P. Samborne took possession of the site on 10 June, he being the landowner, and the plant was accordingly offered to him for its value of £2,354. After some dispute, Samborne bought the plant and, by 1856, the colliery was back at work.

Not for long, however. In May 1858 the proprietors questioned 'the propriety of keeping open [the] colliery under its existing unprofitable circumstances'. Exploration 'in the deep of the Woody Haygrove and Haygrove Engine old workings' was discounted and in or about 1862 the colliery was closed for good. A chicken farm now occupies the pit yard, but the major surviving building, the pumping engine house, has been neatly restored as a dwelling house. The two shafts are also visible.

MEARNS COLLIERY

On 1 May 1783 three leases, all granting permission to 'sink, search and make levels' were drawn up among eight partners who were to be the proprietors in Mearns Colliery.[15] The

shares were laid down in the articles of partnership, signed
on 2 May 1783:

Jacob Mogg	7/32	Robert Langford	3/32
John Crang	7/32	Henry Fisher	2/32
William Savage	4/32	Christian Hill	3/32
Alexander Adams	4/32	William Short	2/32

The pit was doubtless opened soon after this. In 1792,
William Smith surveyed the colliery and his description has
been published elsewhere.[16] He reported an average output of
about 20 tons per day, with a workforce of sixteen men and
five or six boys.

Joseph Hill acquired shares in the pit in 1802 and 1807,
but, because the lessors required the partners to abandon the
pit and begin mining at Woody Heighgrove, Hill sold his
shares to Jacob Mogg in order to avoid the expense of this
removal.[17] The transfer was carried out on 8 November 1817
and the pit appears to have closed shortly afterwards; at least,
no later references to it are known and the lease was due to
expire in 1824. Today, houses have been erected on the pit
site and only the dirt tip remains.

AMESBURY COLLIERY
In 1701 there were 'several hand worked or horse pumps be-
longing to Mr Holland at Amesbury', presumably at the colliery, and the pit was still at work a century later. In 1801,
John Crang bought shares in it for £450, but the pit closed in
the early 1800s. The shaft was about 200ft deep. Amesbury
coal was probably worked from New Tyning pit in 1838, the
water flooding Amesbury having been removed by the pumps
at Hayeswood Colliery. Only the batch and shaft can be seen
today.

BROMBEL OR BROMBELLS COLLIERY
This group of old shafts appears to correspond to Allens Paddock Coal Work mentioned on the SCC-deposited plans of
1793. There are today a great number of old shafts in the area;
one of these was of 4ft 6in diameter, another 6ft x 5ft. It was
intended that Allens Paddock should be served by a tramroad,

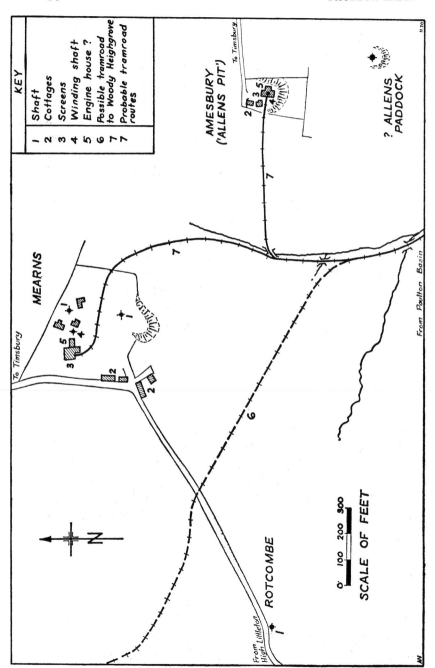

KEY

1	Shaft
2	Cottages
3	Screens
4	Winding shaft
5	Engine house ?
6	Possible tramroad to Woody Heighgrove
7	Probable tramroad routes

To Timsbury

MEARNS

AMESBURY ('ALLENS PIT')

To Timsbury

? ALLENS PADDOCK

ROTCOMBE

From Littleton

From High Littleton

From Paulton Basin

N

SCALE OF FEET

0 100 200 300

but it is unlikely that this was ever built.

HEIGHGROVE COLLIERIES
Heighgrove Colliery was founded in 1753 by John Bush and taken over in 1771 by the Heighgrove Coal Co. In 1791, the pit had been 'long noted for admirable fuel'. The last recorded freeshare payment (to the Popham estates) was in 1819, when the pits had become uneconomic and were to be closed.[18]

There were actually three sites: Heighgrove, Heighgrove Engine, and Woody (or Wooddy) Heighgrove, which together produced between 9,000 and 13,500 tons of coal per year in the mid-eighteenth century. It is likely that a tramroad was laid to Woody Heighgrove; the route is clearly defined even today and a local resident states that the line was laid. No certain evidence of this has been found, the only remains of the colliery today being the tree-covered dirt tip, one of the largest at these early collieries.

WITHY MILLS COLLIERY
Withy Mills was leased on 25 March 1815 by George Mogg, John Parish, William Savage, George Adams, Robert and William Bush, and Gratiana Palmer, the lease stating that they had 'lately begun and opened . . . pits for the discovering and landing of coal' at West Field.[19] It has been suggested that the pit was opened in 1804 but it is unlikely that the word 'lately' would encompass such a length of time.

Coal was wound in hudges but by 1861 cages and guides had been introduced. A $6\frac{1}{2}$in wide flat rope was used for winding in 1841. There were both winding and pumping engines at the pit; in 1852 the proprietors considered purchasing the pumping engine from Paulton Engine Colliery and by February 1853 this was in the course of erection. A new cylinder 96in x 60in was required for this engine and in May 1853 William Evans offered to put it in working order for £650.

When the pit was opened, a self-acting incline was constructed to carry the coal down to the SCC. This line was double track and laid with stone blocks and 'L' tramplates.

A serious accident occurred at the colliery (possibly in the

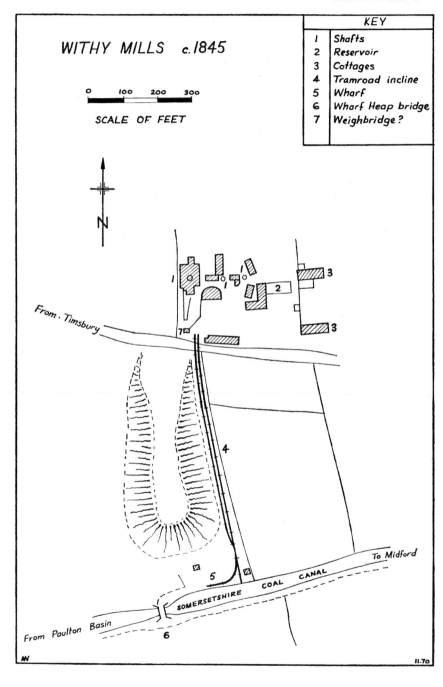

WITHY MILLS c.1845

SCALE OF FEET
0   100   200   300

N

KEY

1	Shafts
2	Reservoir
3	Cottages
4	Tramroad incline
5	Wharf
6	Wharf Heap bridge
7	Weighbridge ?

From. Timsbury

To Midford

SOMERSETSHIRE   COAL   CANAL

From Paulton Basin

11.7o

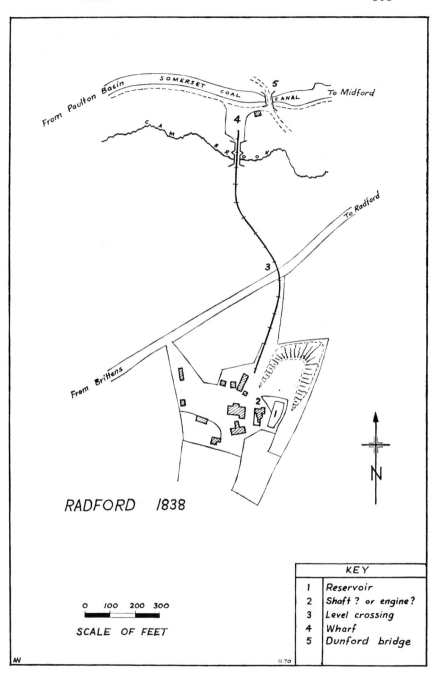

RADFORD 1838

SCALE OF FEET

KEY	
1	Reservoir
2	Shaft ? or engine?
3	Level crossing
4	Wharf
5	Dunford bridge

1850s), involving fatal injuries to nine men. The story goes that the engineman had come on duty much the worse for drink. When he drew up a load of men who, as was common practice, were hanging on to loops on the rope, he overwound them and they came to grief in the wheel, 'coming off like monkeys' according to the account. For this, the driver was rewarded with two years in prison.

In 1872, the pit was still at work, there being about 120 men employed there (including the total at Old Grove),[20] but by December 1877 the pit had shut. William Rees-Mogg, the lessor, assessed surface damage for compensation and he resumed possession of the land on 25 March 1878.[21] Very few traces remain today, apart from the prominent dirt tip. The site of the pit has been obliterated but stone blocks can still be seen *in situ* on the incline; excavations have revealed a turnout with wood and stone sleepers and three tramplates still in position.

RADFORD COLLIERY

This pit, the most easterly of those round Paulton basin, was described as 'Radford New Coal Work' in 1793; it was certainly opened by 1809. After the canal was opened, a tramroad incline was laid up to the pit. It is probable that this was a gravity incline, full wagons drawing up empties, but a local resident states that his grandfather remembered horses drawing six or seven coal trams along the line. A grooved wheel, which would once have carried the incline rope, was unearthed on the track bed during recent excavations.

There were two shafts, each 6ft in diameter and 1,152ft deep, among the deepest in the area. Throughout its existence the pit was owned by the Radford Coal Co, and it is said to have closed in 1847, though the company remained in existence, receiving a payment of £100 in February 1853. Very few traces remain today other than the tree-covered batch and one of the shafts. The tramroad bridge over the Cam Brook has been demolished but the rest of the track bed is fairly clear. One of the tramplates has been preserved.

Notes begin on page 267.

Page 103 A rare view of Clandown Colliery, taken in 1908. Note the unusual arrangement of the pulley wheels (left), the boiler chimney (centre) and the 'chimney' around the furnace shaft (right)

Page 104 (above) Old Mills Colliery in 1967; (below) Ludlows Pit about 1930. The pithead baths were later built on the open site in the foreground

6 TIMSBURY AND CAMERTON

THE TIMSBURY COLLIERIES

In 1791 the first of the Timsbury (Conygre) collieries was sunk on the outskirts of Timsbury village. Known as Conygre (Conigre in some old spellings) it was the culmination of many years of co-operation by the greatest coalmining partnership in Somerset. Generally termed the Timsbury Coal Proprietors and, specifically in this instance, the Conygre Coal Co, the name was changed about 1865 to Samborne Smith & Co after the two main partners, Samborne Stukely Palmer Samborne and Stanley B. Smith. The original partners were Samborne Palmer, Jacob Mogg, William and John Crang (jointly), Alexander Adams and James Savage; Savage held a 4/32 share and the others 7/32.

As the years passed the subdivision of shares reached ridiculous proportions; the limit was possibly the 7/500 of 10/64 held by Miss Sarah Mogg. This was one reason why, in 1897, it was suggested that a limited liability company should be formed to operate the two existing pits at Upper and Lower Conygre. This was never done; S. S. P. Samborne died in 1904 and, following share purchases by the Kennedy family, the title of the business was changed on 1 May 1908 to Beaumont, Kennedy & Co. In 1913, the official title was altered to Kennedy & Co.[1]

The collieries ran on a spartan budget but were usually profitable. Possibly the best year was 1889, the second half of which produced a profit of nearly £2,200. Dividends were suspended in 1897 and it was 1900 before another (£1,000) was paid. In 1903, the total value of the undertaking was £21,915.

G

Timsbury, once the biggest single suppliers to the consumers of Bath, was one of the last Somerset pits to operate in the
autocratic Victorian style, being run under the 1791 partnership agreement throughout. After 1900 the company's fortunes
suffered a drastic downturn and one cannot help but sympa-
thise with the proprietors as they suffered in turn from the
inadequacy of the SCC, the failure of exploration and conse-
quent needless expenditure on modernisation, and a collapse
of the Bath trade, which was closely followed by a series of
labour disputes and, finally, the drowning-out of Lower
Conygre.

In the 1800s the partners were adventurous and successful
but, as the years went by, a family tradition stretching back
nearly two centuries began to atrophy. Expectations failed to
materialise, decisions were taken too slowly and too late, and
the partners grew too poor to extricate themselves by taking
rapid advantage of the arrival of the railway, the last straw
they could have clutched at. In 1916, one of the best known
and most respected collieries in Somerset sadly but inevitably
passed into history.

Upper Conygre Colliery

On 24 January 1791 the partnership agreement for the sinking
of this pit was signed by the six proprietors. Shortly after the
opening, the pit achieved fame by drawing up the shaft a
single lump of coal weighing over 25cwt: 'This ponderous
body was brought from the bottom of the pit to its surface by
the amazing power of steam only'.

The colliery was designed so as to minimise interference
with the view from Timsbury Manor, a venerable residence
built in 1610 and demolished in 1961. The main embellish-
ment was a castellated chimney but a false boundary was also
created, consisting of two parallel stone walls with the intervening space filled with small coal and planted on the top with
trees. Many years later, during a strike, miners noticed the
coal in a place where the wall had fallen down, upon which a
large proportion of the wall's contents disappeared into the
local fireplaces!

Coal disposal was almost entirely by road until Lower
Conygre was opened in 1858, when small coal was sent there
for loading on to the SCC. A traction engine was purchased in
1906 to expedite the Bath land trade but, by the following
year, demand had so fallen off that the engine could not be
kept fully employed.

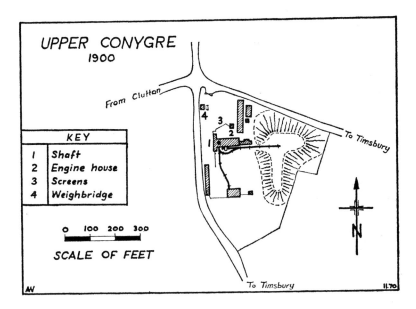

When Lower Conygre opened, an underground connection
was made between the two collieries, and the newer pit soon
began to overshadow its forbear. The Upper Conygre downcast shaft collapsed and ventilation was altered to make the
two Lower Conygre shafts downcast and the remaining Upper
shaft upcast.

During the night maintenance shift on Wednesday 6 February 1895 there was a disastrous underground explosion mid-
way between the two pits.[2] Seven men and four horses were
killed, while the force was such that the cage at Upper Conygre was blown up the shaft, becoming jammed as it fell back.
A rescue party formed of six local colliery managers found a
scene of terrible confusion, with props blown away, roof falls,
and shattered tubs. The seven men had been killed instantly.

The inquest of 4 March 1895 found the explosion to be due to airborne coal dust, as at Camerton two years earlier. The company was absolved from blame and, in view of this, it is of interest to note that a few months before the explosion the company had taken special note of a report by the Inspector of Mines which emphasised the 'necessity of taking proper precautions to avoid explosion from coal dust in connection with shot firing. . .'

There were few changes at the pit, for it was not modernised as was Lower Conygre. However, when that pit was flooded in 1914, Upper Conygre became the last working colliery in Timsbury. In 1916, before a proposal to reopen the collapsed downcast shaft could be effected, the coal faces ran into a major fault and the pit was closed for good. Very few traces remain today, for the site is now occupied by a breeze-block factory. Remnants of the wall of the engine house have been incorporated into new buildings, while a couple of small huts survive as stores.

Lower Conygre Colliery

On 27 April 1847, Major Savage informed his partners that he intended to sink a 'new Coal work' within the boundaries of the existing lease of Upper Conygre. The idea met an early setback when it was found that no banker was prepared to lend money because of the advanced ages of the partners; however, the money was raised, and by 16 October 1848 the first shaft had been sunk to about two-thirds of its intended depth. In June 1849, after declining to buy the surplus winding engine at Farmborough Colliery, the proprietors accepted William Evans' tender of £920 for erection of a new engine, to be ready for use by 1 March 1850.

Money now ran short and in September 1850 consideration was given to halting the work; Evans had not completed the winding engine which, in October, was said to be poorly installed. It was not until August 1851 that money had been found and the sinking of the second shaft begun.

To connect the colliery to the SCC a tramway was laid in 1855-6 but was not brought into use until 1859. Coal winding at Lower Conygre appears to have started about December 1858, more than a decade after work had begun at the site. This did not please the proprietors overmuch, nor was Evans exactly satisfied with his part in the venture. His book-keeping proved to be as faulty as his engine-erecting for he found that, due to a mistake in his calculations, he had lost £50 on the contract. He was, rather generously, allowed an extra £25.

The two shafts were sunk south of Upper Conygre. A single cage was used in each shaft, the winding engine being sited between them, and a flat woven-steel rope, $3\frac{1}{2}$in wide and $\frac{3}{4}$in thick, was wound on each drum of the engine. From the top of the western shaft, the 2ft $4\frac{1}{2}$in gauge incline ran down to serve the landsale depot and on to the SCC wharf. There were coke ovens at the depot in the 1860s, but they had fallen out of use by the 1890s.

By the 1880s the inadequacy of the canal was becoming increasingly apparent and in May 1894 the proprietors decided to obtain a siding from the GWR to serve the pit. They met with difficulties in acquiring the necessary land but, even so, the work took an excessively long time. Construction of the sidings and incline up to the colliery began in September 1898, and the self-acting incline was opened for traffic in October 1900. The narrow-gauge incline remained in use down to the coal depot until February 1906 when it was decided to remove the rails and use the track-bed as a dirt tip.

Straddling this period were two abortive attempts at development. In 1887 a branch was begun with the intention of proving coal to the north of the Farmborough Fault. Work continued throughout 1892-3 but no commercial amounts of coal were found. On 10 June 1895, after the mineral owner had refused to grant the company an exploration licence, the project was abandoned. However, hopes were not dead yet, for plans were advanced for another underground drift to achieve the same purpose. The work was decided upon in July 1895, the proposal being for two drifts, 1,800ft long and dropping at 16in per yd. It was not an ideal scheme, but the alternatives of deepening Lower Conygre or sinking an entirely new shaft were far too costly.

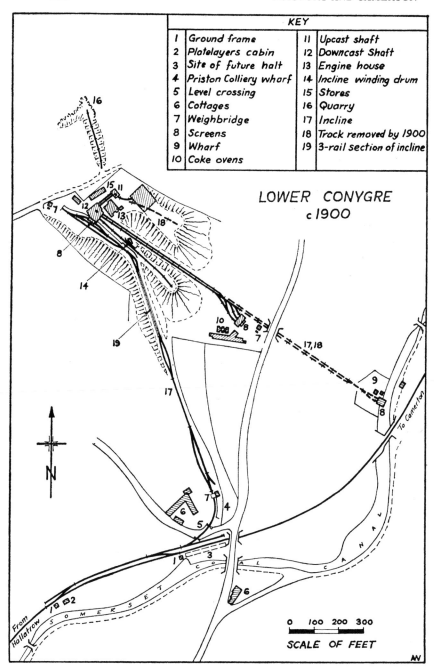

KEY

1	Ground frame	11	Upcast shaft
2	Platelayers cabin	12	Downcast Shaft
3	Site of future halt	13	Engine house
4	Priston Colliery wharf	14	Incline winding drum
5	Level crossing	15	Stores
6	Cottages	16	Quarry
7	Weighbridge	17	Incline
8	Screens	18	Track removed by 1900
9	Wharf	19	3-rail section of incline
10	Coke ovens		

LOWER CONYGRE
c 1900

N

SCALE OF FEET
0   100   200   300

J. Batey, who first suggested the 1887 exploration, was thoroughly critical of this new plan, possibly because James McMurtrie was acting as advisor to the company. Batey's objections made the company think again and work did not actually begin until December 1907, surface modernisations being initiated in the intervening years.

Success came on 21 March 1910 when, after driving 1,980ft, the No 4 Seam was proved. The second drift, which had earlier been halted, was now pushed ahead so as to reach this coal and allow mining to begin. Very soon, however, the initial satisfaction wore off as no more coal was found; on further investigation the No 4 Seam was found to be too faulted to work, and on 1 October 1910 work was abandoned.

The money spent on this work can only be guessed at; on the surface, however, some £4,000 was expended on a new chimney, new boilers, new three-deck cages, and an electricity generating plant for working a haulage engine in the new drift. Without doubt, the failure of this exploration broke both the backs and hearts of the proprietors. To make matters worse, 1911 was a year of labour disputes and a trade recession that lasted into 1912. Lower Conygre was shut down in March 1911 but reopened in July.[3] On 10 January 1912, the men and staff at both Upper and Lower Conygre were discharged and the pits again closed down. By February, however, something approaching normal working had been resumed.[4] Two years later, in March 1914, disaster struck and Lower Conygre was flooded.

Mining in the Radstock Series had been approaching the flooded Withy Mills workings and, because of this, advance boreholes were being put out to detect the water before mining broke into it. The drilling machine was fitted with a tap so that, in the event of water being encountered, it could be shut off. Unfortunately, since the tap tended to hamper the operation of the drill, it had been unofficially removed, with the inevitable result. The Withy Mills workings were holed, the inflow of water could not be shut off, and the entire pit was flooded to within a short distance of shaft bottom. Pumping had no effect, the water level rising slowly but inexorably.

Following geological difficulties at Upper Conygre, the decision was taken to close both pits, which was done in June 1916.

Before concluding we may mention the introduction in 1874 of the first coal-cutting machine in Somerset.[5] One of Frith's patents, it was set to work at Lower Conygre on a coalface 100yd in length, and produced 50 tons of coal per 8-hour shift. Much interest was aroused; at the beginning of April a party of local colliery proprietors saw it at work, and the following day the gentlemen of the press and dignitaries from Bath were accorded a similar privilege. The trial was said to be highly successful and 'conclusively demonstrated the usefullness and effectiveness of the machine'. Toasts were proposed and drunk by both masters and men, 'some of the latter declaring they had never tasted champagne before'; fulsome speeches were made but the machine, in the event, proved a failure.

The pithead has been levelled and tipped on, but there are still numerous traces visible today. The routes of the narrow- and standard-gauge inclines can be seen, the haulage rope still lying on the latter, while the site of the coal depot, though now grassed over, is also discernible. At the foot of the standard-gauge incline is the retaining wall where coal from Priston Colliery was tipped into railway trucks, this traffic being worked for some years after Lower Conygre closed. At the pithead, the concrete cap of the western shaft, the concrete base and fixing bolts of the dynamo, and the drift that once provided water for the boilers, can all be found. The overgrown dirt tips and pithead, indeed, are as inaccessible today as they were when the contractors struggled to bring machinery to the colliery for the modernisation that lasted so few years, and are happily likely to remain so.

THE CAMERTON COLLIERIES
The lease for the first of the two Camerton pits was granted by James Stephens on 13 November 1781.[6] By 1800, the second or New Pit had been sunk, a few hundred yards to the east of Old Pit. The two collieries were connected underground, and

by surface tramways. Coal was disposed of by road until the construction of the SCC; in October 1798 this was opened between Camerton and Dunkerton and Camerton coal was sent to Dunkerton by canal and thence to Bath, the principal market, by road.

The 1781 lease allocated the original shares in the collieries as follows:

James Stephens*	5/22	Thomas Tyley	2/22
Zachary Bailey	8/22	Moses Reynolds	1/22
Peter Fry	5/22	Joseph Rose	1/22

*Also received freeshare of 1/8 as the lessor.

On 20 April 1801 a marriage settlement was made between Stephens (lord of the manor of Camerton) and the Jarrett family on the occasion of the marriage of Stephens' daughter to Herbert Jarrett, and by this the Jarretts gained both the manor and the mines.[7] Under Anne Jarrett's will of 13 July 1822, the collieries passed to her nephew, John Jarrett. To help the collieries become more profitable, Jarrett reduced his rate of freeshare to one-tenth in 1833 but in 1843, when asked to accept a further reduction to one-twelfth, he refused and the lessees of the pits promptly closed one seam and sacked a number of men.[8] By 1882, Anna Mary Jarrett was the owner of the pits, though her sister Emily controlled them in practice. After Lady Emily's death in December 1911 the collieries were bought by Sir Frank Beauchamp.

Financially, the pits were in a good state in the early 1800s. Between 1830 and 1843, profits totalled £16,761 against losses of £1,741; £11,576 was disbursed as dividends. In 1843 one John Smith reported on the undertaking.[9] After describing development work at Old Pit, he concluded, 'the prospects are discouraging'. He further commented that 'it is not advisable to sink the pits to the 2nd Series of Coal Seams but I believe they prove under the Pits'.

Prospects were not in fact as discouraging as he thought, for the pits continued successfully. The opening of the GWR branch line from Hallatrow provided a means of transport much superior to the canal and a siding was built into New

Pit by an agreement of 5 September 1882, at an estimated cost of £157.

Camerton remained unaffected by the 1893 labour disputes and in fact the men received a 7½ per cent increase in wages. Possibly the freedom from dispute was unfortunate; at midnight on 13-14 November 1893, two men were killed in an underground explosion so devastating as to block the New Pit shaft at a depth of 750ft.[10] At first the cause of the explosion was a mystery but it was eventually established that shot firing by the men had ignited coal dust in the mine's atmosphere. This was the first such explosion in Somerset and the causes provided much material for scientific debate. Nor was this the end of Camerton's troubles. In December, soon after the end of the strike, the Camerton men were asked to give up the 7½ per cent increase they had so lately obtained, and it seems likely that the increase was given purely as a way of avoiding a strike at the pits.

Old Pit was closed for coal winding about 1898 but remained open as an airway and escape route for New Pit. In 1928-30 an underground road was driven from Braysdown Colliery to New Pit, thus providing an alternative airway (which was duplicated after 1937) and Old Pit was entirely closed and dismantled when the first connection was made.

As at other collieries, the late 1800s were halcyon days for Camerton. In the period from 1888 to 1900, coal landings had doubled to over 70,000 tons pa, receipts rising from £17,000 to £40,000 pa. The maximum known output was 76,827 tons in 1903; the highest receipts, £62,208 in 1924.[11]

The New Pit winding engine in the 1900s was a two-cylinder (26in x 54in) horizontal type built by the Leeds Engineering Co in 1895 to replace the first engine at the pit. Dirt was tipped on a batch between the canal and the Cam Brook but, soon after 1902, tipping on the canal bed began, producing the huge conical dirt tip that is even today such a prominent feature of the valley. There were two tramways of about 2ft 4in gauge running from the pithead; that to Old Pit was removed about 1910 and converted into a road. The second served Meadgate coal depot by an incline worked by a 50hp endless-rope haulage motor. Meadgate was the landsales depot; for rail disposal of coal there was only limited siding accommodation and, up to 1947, shunting was performed by horses, other than in a brief period about 1926 when *Dunkerton* from Dunkerton Colliery came for trials. These were unsuccessful and the locomotive is believed to have gone to Norton Hill Colliery after a few months.

In 1946, the colliery was valued at £59,935, the lowest figure of the Somerset Collieries Ltd pits. Between 1937 and 1946, profits had averaged £2,583pa, similar to those of a century earlier.[12] Underground, the pit was almost unchanged since opening. All coal was got by hand, 60 per cent of it travelling in tubs to the shaft; this limited the potential output to 300 tons per day, though the actual output was less than half this figure. In fact, output during the 1930s was almost exactly the same as in the 1830s.

Once the pit was nationalised, some modernisation was begun. A road tractor replaced the horses in the sidings, while the use of conveyors underground was extended. A new canteen was opened, as it turned out, only nine months before closure. In order to improve the pit's performance, the south district workings were closed in December 1949, making thirty men redundant. This move, part of the NCB's policy of concentrating production at a single point, did not help the pit to become profitable and 135 men received their notices on 6 April 1950. With the winding of the last coal on the morning shift of 14 April, the colliery closed. Salvage continued until August, the pit being officially closed in September and the remaining twenty-five men discharged.

The main reason for closure was the exhaustion of accessible reserves, Camerton being the last colliery in Somerset to work Radstock Series coal. Efforts had been made to discover new reserves but the ghost of John Smith seemed to haunt these attempts. Prior to 1886 the downcast shaft was deepened to a total depth of 1,818ft, the intention being to work the Farrington seams. An exploratory crossmeasure drift was driven from pit bottom and the first coal was produced in the second half of 1913. Five years later, these deep workings were closed, only

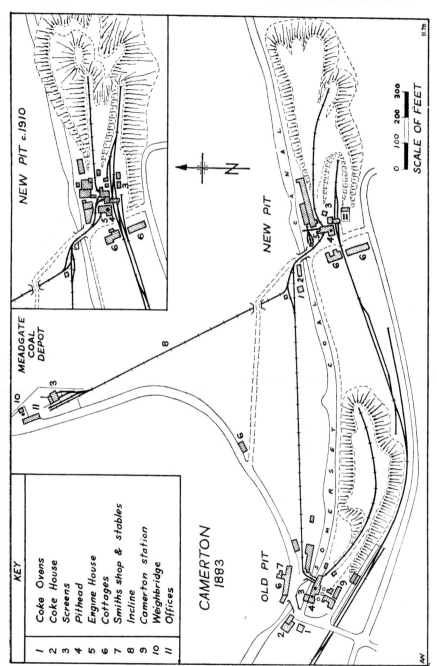

NEW PIT c.1910

KEY

1	Coke Ovens
2	Coke House
3	Screens
4	Pithead
5	Engine House
6	Cottages
7	Smiths shop & stables
8	Incline
9	Camerton station
10	Weighbridge
11	Offices

CAMERTON
1883

MEADGATE
COAL
DEPOT

NEW PIT

OLD PIT

SOMERSET   COAL   CANAL

SCALE OF FEET

0   100   200   300

2,015 tons of coal having been raised from them. Further development work was carried out by Sir Frank Beauchamp in April 1941, but no coal was raised. In 1946 a scheme was put forward whereby Dunkerton would be reopened and connected to Camerton, an output of 200,000 tons per year being contemplated. But John Smith was right; the Farrington seams never came into production and Camerton, the last colliery in the Cam Valley, was closed.

There are several traces of the two pits today. Old Pit is much overgrown and only the adjacent canal bed can be clearly seen. Hidden in the undergrowth, however, are the crumbling foundations of some of the pithead buildings. At New Pit, the screens have been demolished but the heapstead wall still stands. There is a concrete cap over the downcast shaft and the foundations of the headgear are still in situ. Until 1968 the foundations of the engine house and the canal bed could be seen but these have been obliterated by rubbish tipping. The canteen survives as a dwelling house, while the track beds of the standard- and narrow-gauge lines are intact, as are many of the buildings at Meadgate coal depot. The most prominent relic, however, is the huge dirt tip from which, on a fine day, first-class views over the valley may be obtained.

Notes begin on page 267.

7 EAST OF CAMERTON

Eastwards from Camerton, the coal is overlain by a considerable depth of newer strata and for many centuries there was no certainty that coal in fact was present. Up to the twentieth century, only two mines—both failures—were sunk; by then, however, geological suspicions were strong probabilities and two collieries were opened, Dunkerton and Priston. Both should have been successes but, for various reasons, both had closed by 1930. As an introduction to these, we shall deal first with the two early pits.

BENGROVE AND HILL'S COLLIERIES
These are the subject of considerable confusion. Neither appears to have worked for more than a few years, and each was variously titled. It is believed that Bengrove was otherwise known as Priston Old and Dunkerton; and that Hill's was alternatively Priston and Dunkerton New. The names Priston and Dunkerton should not be confused with the modern collieries. Bengrove was sunk in 1764-5 and was 506ft deep, and Hill's was sunk in 1792-3.[1] Bengrove was closed after perhaps a decade, while Hill's appears to have survived to at least 1824.

Both pits were intended to be connected to the SCC by tramroads, suggesting that Bengrove was to be reopened. Earthworks for the incline up to Hill's were completed but investigations on the site suggest that no coal was carried on the tramroad and it was probably never completed. Because of a lack of direct contemporary evidence, it would be unwise to speculate further.

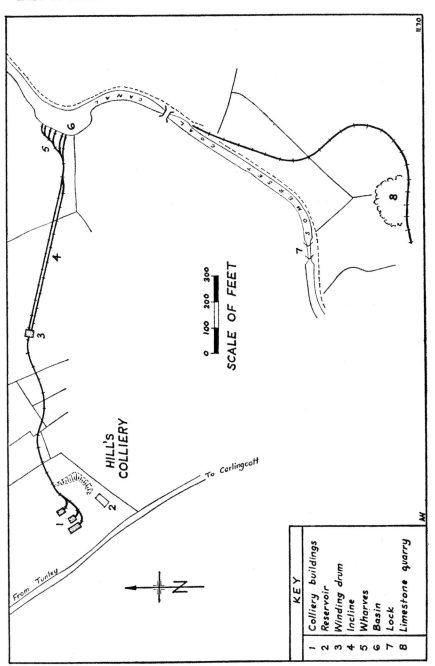

SCALE OF FEET

0   100   200   300

HILL'S COLLIERY

To Carlingcott

From Tunley

N

KEY

1   Colliery buildings
2   Reservoir
3   Winding drum
4   Incline
5   Wharves
6   Basin
7   Lock
8   Limestone quarry

DUNKERTON COLLIERY

The story of Dunkerton is one of the most remarkable in the coalfield. In its short working life, only about twenty years, the pit became both the largest in Somerset and the one with the worst reputation among the men who worked there.

Plans for the colliery were in hand in 1898[2] and the contract for sinking the first shaft was signed on 11 May 1903 by Dunkerton Collieries Ltd (Matthew Watson, Egbert Spear and W. J. Heppel) and the Radstock partnership of George, Frederick and Alfred Dowling.[3] Twelve months were allowed for completion of the sinking but massive influxes of water (up to 130,000gph) caused considerable delays and in October 1903 all the sinkers were out of work until, exactly a year later, the water was overcome.[4] During this period, sinking of the second shaft was begun. Work was completed in 1906.

Construction of the GWR Camerton to Limpley Stoke branch, authorised under an Act of 1904, was subject to some delays but the line from Camerton had certainly reached the colliery by 1907, coal trains being despatched after 4 April.[5] The first coal, found in 1905, was disposed of by road in 1906 and, up to 1910, many of the working arrangements were of a temporary nature. The railway sidings, for example, were worked by a stationary haulage engine until, on 8 August 1910, a new shunting locomotive named *Dunkerton* was delivered from Peckett & Sons of Bristol. The engine had been completed in April 1909, which suggests that it was not delivered until the sidings were completed.

Dunkerton earned its bad name from the company's sole concern of getting coal as quickly and as cheaply as possible, to which end a coal-cutting machine was introduced about June 1910. At the peak of working in 1912, over 700 men were employed and about 3,000 tons of coal raised each week. Indeed, the colliery manager is said to have received a gold watch when 5,000 tons was raised in a week. The effect of this scale of production—and the way in which it was achieved—was that only coal easy to get was mined and areas of poorer, thinner or less accessible coal were left scattered over the royalty. There was a disregard for safety and a common sight at the pithead was a small cart, drawn by a white pony, which took killed or injured men back to their homes. It was such conditions that made the riots at Dunkerton during the 1908-9 strike some of the worst in the history of the coalfield.

The riots had their origins in the early months of 1907.[6] On 13 April the carting boys, of whom there were nearly 200 at Dunkerton, applied for an increase in wages on the grounds that the roads were rougher and the putts heavier than at other pits. The pay of these lads, who were between 16 and 22 years of age, was then 1d per ton for the first 50yd of haulage and $\frac{1}{2}$d per ton for each subsequent 50yd; they wished this second rate to be increased to 1d, but the company would not grant it. The dispute lasted for eighteen months until, on 29 October 1908, the carting boys lost patience and struck work. Apart from about sixty men who remained at work on exploration and maintenance, the remaining labour force followed suit, partly from sympathy and partly from necessity, since, without the carting boys, no coal could be brought to land.

There was a great deal of ill-feeling against those who remained at work and detachments of foot and mounted police were drafted to the area in case of trouble. For three months things were peaceful, but on Friday 22 January 1909 an 'outrage' occurred.[7]

It is usually difficult to diagnose the causes of mob violence but the incident that sparked off the trouble appears to have been this: on Friday afternoon, the manager's son, Edgar Heal (who was also the colliery surveyor), told two non-strikers not to be worried by the hostile crowds that often met them at the pithead after work and shouted their disapproval of 'blacklegs'. This conversation was overheard by some militant strikers, who determined to show that there was, in fact, good cause to be worried. Throughout the afternoon they rallied their forces for a demonstration march through Carlingcott and, after scattered incidents of vandalism, some 200 carting boys and miners assembled on the village outskirts. Charles Heal (the colliery manager) had heard of the impending march and had gone to Radstock in an unsuccessful attempt to persuade the miners' agent to come and calm the men down. At 6.15 that

H

evening, while Mr Heal was still in Radstock, the strikers
began to march through Carlingcott towards Heal's house in
Vernal Lane, thinking he would be at home; in fact, the only
occupants were Edgar and his sister, Mrs Heal and one of the
manager's brothers-in-law who was there on a visit. Edgar,
therefore, was the man of the house, and, seeing the approaching mob hurling stones through the windows of roadside
houses, not unnaturally was alarmed. After the event, Edgar
(who was then only 21) admitted: 'I was in great terror'. In
an effort to safeguard the premises and the women inside he
rushed to the door and fired two revolver shots into the air,
partly as a warning to the mob and partly to attract the attention of the police. The mob replied with a hail of stones, so he
went back into the house and loaded his father's shotgun.
Seeing that the rioters had no intention of halting their advance, he fired three or four times into the mob.

Subsequent events are confused. It is variously reported that
this quelled the mob, who stopped to attend to their wounded
comrades, or that the police arrived and turned back the advance. In either event, Edgar shepherded his mother and sister
out of the back door and across the fields to safety, while his
uncle remained hidden in the house to inform Mr Heal of
what had occurred. Having seen the women to safety, Edgar
vanished in fear of his life. On Saturday he telephoned to say
that he was in Bristol and asked his father to inform the police.
This was done, Edgar was arrested on a charge of unlawful
and malicious wounding, and was detained in prison at
Weston-super-Mare.

About twelve men were injured in the shooting. They
strongly denied that any of the strikers had been armed, which,
so far as it referred to firearms, was true. All through Saturday
the after-effects of the shooting were felt. One worker needed
an escort of twenty policemen before he could safely leave the
colliery and even then his house was stoned. Another man and
his escort were waylaid and two constables were injured. Over
the two days, twenty-one men were arrested on charges of
rioting.

The cases arising from the troubles were referred to the

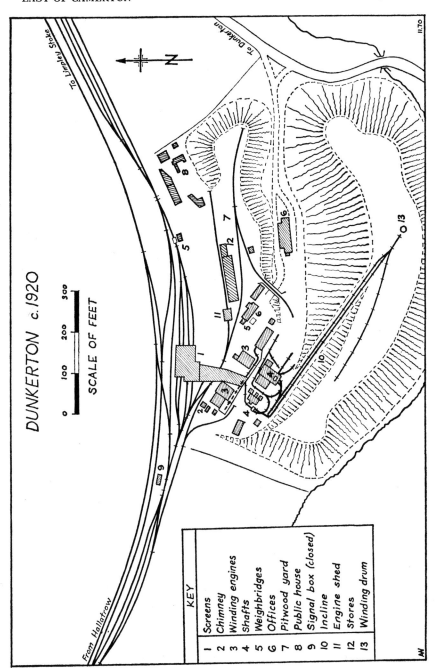

DUNKERTON c.1920

SCALE OF FEET

0   100   200   300

KEY

1 Screens
2 Chimney
3 Winding engines
4 Shafts
5 Weighbridges
6 Offices
7 Pitwood yard
8 Public house
9 Signal box (closed)
10 Incline
11 Engine shed
12 Stores
13 Winding drum

To Limpley Stoke

To Dunkerton

From Hallatrow

N

Winter Assize Court at Taunton, the hearings beginning on 26 February 1909 when twelve colliers were tried. Two were discharged, seven received three months' imprisonment and three, six months', all with hard labour. On 30 March, Edgar Heal was put into the dock and acquitted. He then asked for leniency to be shown to the remaining ten miners, who were tried the next day. Five were found guilty. As regards the strike itself it had ended, following arbitration, in the last week of February and so, finally, all was peaceful.

Animosity was directed at Charles Heal during the troubles, though with no good reason. Other pits with which Mr Heal was connected were operated in a proper manner and there seems little doubt that he did his best under very difficult circumstances. Mr Heal, remembered locally for his bowler hat and gamp, was a 'local boy made good' and it is unlikely that he was in any way responsible for the conditions at Dunkerton.

To return to the colliery, mining was proceeding at such a rate that by July 1915 the No 1 shaft was deepened to cut the Radstock seams below the Middle Vein and to start mining in the Farrington seams, the shaft reaching 1,651ft in depth. Both shafts were thereafter used for coal winding, which helps to explain the very high outputs that the pit could achieve. An elaborate tub circuit linked the two shafts with the screens, up to which tubs were run on a creeper roadway, possibly the first in Somerset.

In February 1920, the pit ran into financial difficulties and its closure was contemplated,[8] but averted in this instance, and again in January 1922, but, after several false alarms in 1925, the last coal was wound by the morning shift on Saturday 30 May 1925.[9] Some underground salvage continued until September, when Dunkerton Collieries Ltd ceased their activities at the pit. The reason for this closure was primarily the exhaustion of accessible coal, due to the short-sighted policies pursued by the company in earlier years. It is said that royalty problems with the Daniels family leases also contributed towards the closure.

Negotiations were begun by Sir Frank Beauchamp to try

DUNKERTON COLLIERY
May 6th, 1925

Mr. *Geo Sage (Jnr)*

I hereby give you notice that this Company will not require your services after one week from this date.

For and on behalf of the
DUNKERTON COLLIERIES LTD.

S S Bawley ....Manager

and acquire the colliery and, by the end of 1925, most of the leases had been transferred to his name.[10] Sir Frank worked the pit in a small way but, on 30 August 1927, the men were given notice and on 6 September the pit was shut down for the last time. Only 4,000 tons of coal were wound at Dunkerton under Sir Frank's ownership. The reason for this is that Sir Frank had no real intention of ever working the pit; it was acquired to prevent flooding of the Camerton Colliery workings and to provide coal reserves for Priston.

Even though the pit was closed and rapidly becoming derelict, it was still the subject of innumerable reopening schemes.[11] In May 1928 a group of former employees made enquiries, but in February 1929 Sir Frank decided to dismantle the surface works entirely. He appointed Lot Sampson to survey the pit preparatory to winding the coal at Priston, and Sampson was obviously so taken with the pit's possibilities that he, too, produced a plan to reopen it. This also came to nothing. On 22 March 1929 a more definite scheme was produced, one Major Mackintosh being in charge of it. The idea was that the pit would be reopened and leased to a group of unemployed miners. Sir Frank was willing to help and, after suggesting an extortionate rental, eventually agreed to give the men a free loan of anything they required. Official sanction of all this was apparently not forthcoming, for the plans were abandoned.

With this failure, the colliery equipment was gradually transferred to other pits owned by Somerset Collieries Ltd. Dunkerton Coal Factors Ltd retained their depot in the colliery yard for many years, however, bringing coal from other pits to fulfil their orders.

During World War II came the final two proposals for re-opening the colliery. Somerset Collieries Ltd proposed in 1941 to work the remaining Radstock Series coal from Braysdown and Camerton, while using the Dunkerton shafts to wind the largely intact Farrington Series.[12] The plan fell through but was revived by the NCB in a slightly different form.[13] In October 1946 they suggested that the Dunkerton and Camerton deep shafts should be sunk to the No 7 seam, a connection made between them, and 200,000 tons of coal wound from them each year. But nothing came of this, and finally Dunkerton ceased to be the subject of abortive proposals.

The colliery site is still largely intact, though every scrap of metal was salvaged during the war. It is currently occupied by a haulage contractor, who uses the locomotive shed and stores as lorry garages. The winding engine houses are largely intact, while the colliery offices, virtually unaltered, serve as offices for the new occupiers.

PRISTON OR TUNLEY COLLIERY[14]

Priston, the last deep mine to be opened in Somerset, was sunk by the lord of the manor of Priston, Captain William Vaughan-Jenkins, and H. Alger. Plans for the sinking, in an area untouched by early workings, were in hand in 1906, E. H. Staples, a noted geologist, being intimately concerned in the venture and, later, colliery manager. Two boreholes, at Priston and Withyditch, were sunk in 1907 to prove the ground, but the chosen site for the sinking was immediately to the west of Tunley village, beside the Bath Road. In 1904, Captain Vaughan-Jenkins had been involved in promoting the Priston Light Railway but the failure of this scheme in its original form meant that the colliery would have to rely mainly on landsales, hence its site.

Work on the sinking was delayed and it was not until the

afternoon of Wednesday, 11 March 1914 that Mrs Vaughan-Jenkins ceremonially turned the first sod of earth and the work began. The sinking was thus carried out during the years of acute shortage of materials occasioned by World War I, which resulted in high prices for essential equipment, though much was obtained secondhand.

The sinking contract was let to G. Dowling, of the group that had recently proved itself at Dunkerton, and up to 23 September 1914 the work had cost £142. Secondhand plant came mainly from J. Pugsley of Bristol—boiler, pumps, winding engine, weighbridge, etc—while nearly half a million bricks were purchased from the Bath Victoria Brick and Tile Co Ltd for walling the shaft. Lime came from Job Hodder's kiln at Timsbury.

At 1am on Whit Sunday morning, 1915, the first coal was found and, at 5am, the first skip of coal was raised to the surface. 'With much glee, a flag pole was quickly erected on the pit top and a Union Jack run up,' while the under-manager, George Mitchard, detailed a man to cycle over to Combe Down to inform Captain Vaughan-Jenkins of the good news. The coal, of the Great Vein, had been found at a depth of 690ft, 140ft deeper than had been anticipated. Coal production began about July 1915, when the shaft had reached its full depth of 750ft. Sinking of the second shaft began in 1916 and the cages began work on 1 December 1917.

One problem was that of coal disposal. Mr Staples produced a scheme to take the whole of the anticipated weekly output (380 tons) by aerial ropeway to the GWR at Dunkerton Colliery, but this was not done and road vehicles were used to carry coal to Radford Wharf at the foot of the old Lower Conygre Colliery incline. Horses were hired to shunt the trucks on this siding, W. Rogers being paid 7s 6d per truck in 1920 and Alfred Mullins 15s per day in 1922.

For road traffic, a 5-ton steam lorry equipped with hydraulic tipping gear was bought from the Sentinel Waggon Works Ltd (their number D2036). In July 1921, the lorry received a new coat of paint and the legend 'Priston Collieries Coy' in gold leaf on the front and sides of the cab. However, despite being the only major item of plant purchased new, the lorry was unreliable and frequently broke down.

From the opening of the colliery, the headgear was of wooden construction. It was painted with red non-inflammable paint but a visiting inspector of mines doubted its non-combustible properties. To prove the point, a piece was chopped out and thrown on the blacksmith's fire where, to the relief of all concerned, it steadfastly refused to burn. Between September 1920 and March 1921 some rebuilding was undertaken and a new ferro-concrete headgear was constructed for £155, thereby allaying any lingering doubts.

Steam was supplied by a Lancashire boiler, supplemented by a Marshall locomotive-type boiler after the arrival of the second winding engine. After 1919, a marine boiler was acquired from a laundry at Hayle, Cornwall, and it was often necessary to couple all three boilers together in order to raise sufficient steam. Consequently, in February 1922, another Lancashire boiler (built by Galloway) was bought from Grace Brothers, a baking firm at Welsh Back, Bristol. The Marshall boiler was then sold to the Farrington drift mine partnership, while the Lancashire boilers were fitted up with Bennett mechanical stokers. The boiler chimney was also a curious feature, constructed from old boiler flues bolted together and looking much like a ship's funnel. It was built by Dawson's of Clutton, doubtless much against their better wishes, and it was only justice when they obtained the contract to build a new brick chimney after 1926.

Priston was never a very successful pit, due to an economy budget when sinking and the unfortunate effects of World War I; apart from a motley collection of secondhand equipment, there had been insufficient money to lay out the underground workings for a large output. Finally, it was decided to sell the pit as a going concern and it was bought by Sir Frank Beauchamp in February 1923.

Sir Frank bought Priston both for working in its own right and to provide coal reserves for his Camerton Colliery. A third use for Priston arose when Sir Frank acquired Dunkerton Colliery, it being proposed that Dunkerton coal be wound at

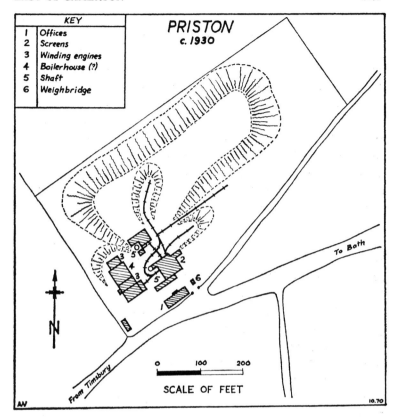

KEY	
1	Offices
2	Screens
3	Winding engines
4	Boilerhouse (?)
5	Shaft
6	Weighbridge

PRISTON
c. 1930

To Bath

From Timsbury

0   100   200
SCALE OF FEET

Priston. It is not known why this scheme was not adopted in reverse, since Priston had nothing to commend it as a coal-winding shaft, whereas Dunkerton had every facility. In point of fact, little coal was wound at Priston—only 50,000 tons up to June 1930.

Priston was closed for the duration of the 1926 strike, during which the union, mindful of the need to preserve its members' jobs, allowed some coal to be wound in order to keep the boilers in steam. Sir Frank was not so conscious of this need and on 19 June he issued a warning to the Priston men (and those at Dunkerton and Middle Pit) that unless they resumed work immediately the pit would be permanently closed. The men refused and Sir Frank ordered them to begin dismantling the colliery; this they likewise refused to do and so the pit reopened after this very lengthy strike.

Sir Frank's main works at Priston were exploratory, and even these were frequently interrupted by the failure of the more decrepit items of machinery. In 1928 a branch was begun in the Top Little Vein and driven downwards at 1 in $3\frac{1}{2}$ to prove, at the cessation of driving on 16 September 1929, seven seams. Little coal was worked, because there was extreme faulting. Beauchamp stated that the explorations had lost him 'thousands of pounds'. He also tried to work Dunkerton coal; the connection between the Priston Top Little Vein and the Dunkerton Middle Vein had been made in about June 1925 but was dammed off at the end of 1926.

Closure was considered in August 1927, when the labour force of about 180 men was given notice, but this was rescinded and efforts concentrated on exploration. Before long another definite closure date—April 1929—was announced, but this, too, was ignored. Difficulties were mounting, however: the pit's main customer, Bath gas works, ceased all purchases on 14 August 1929 after suffering a bad fire. On Wednesday, 18 June 1930, the remaining coal-faces were stopped and the pit closed down for good. Dismantling was rapid and by 1932 only a few items of machinery remained. Camerton Colliery worked some Priston coal up to 1938 at least but it was not until 1940 that it was proposed to dismantle the Priston headgear. Apart from the dirt tip, the main surviving relic today is the colliery office, now a dwelling house. Remnants of the screens, foundations of the engine house, and the capped shafts, can all be found in the undergrowth.

Notes begin on page 268.

8 FARRINGTON GURNEY

The history of coalmining in the area east of Farrington Gurney is second in length only to that at Stratton and in both cases there are excellent records surviving from the 1600s and later. At Farrington, the Mogg family stands out above all others and a brief look at the family history will be a convenient starting point for this chapter.

In 1606 occurred the death of John Keene, *alias* Mogge, of Shepton Montague; one of his children was Richard Mogge and it is here that the family connection begins. Richard built Farrington Gurney manor house and in 1618 became bailiff to the Duchy of Cornwall estates, which had fallen to the Crown on the attainder of de Gourney, one of the murderers of Edward II. On 6 July 1633 Richard applied for a licence to explore for coal under the estate and two years later he took out a lease for 21 years, paying freeshare of one-sixth. The mines were unprofitable; in 1639 he successfully applied for a reduction in freeshare to one-tenth but within a few months the mines had closed.[1]

Richard's second son, John (baptised in 1608, died 1677), restarted the mines after the Civil War and his grandson—also John—continued as proprietor in the 1700s. The family connection with mining in north Somerset was maintained well into the 1800s and, to the end of that century, by the Rees-Mogg family.

There were other families mining in the area. By 1660, a Mr Tynte was at work, and he continued (with poor results) up to 1668 when he had obtained 'practically no coal'. Dame Penelope Tynte made an attempt in 1696 to prevent the Mogg family from working the mines; but in this she was unsuccessful.[2] John Mogg, however, began to sublease some of his mines, one going to a partnership formed by John Curtis, Walter Smith, John Tooker and Richard Naish.

We are concerned here with three major collieries; Farrington proper was a Mogg family venture, but Old Mills and Springfield were started by William Evans of Paulton Foundry and were his most successful pits. The Duchy of Cornwall was unconnected with Evans' collieries but intimately involved both with Farrington and with two co-operative drift mines started by unemployed miners in 1921. The unprofitability of the early mines was a contrast to the profitability of Old Mills, one of the most dependable pits in Somerset.

FARRINGTON COLLIERY[3]

The early mines detailed above were all known by this general heading but only one mine survived into the present century. Among the confusion of names it is hard to sort out details from this early period but Farrington appears to have been sunk shortly before 1783.

On 31 May 1785 it was stated that Farrington was looking promising and the same report was made ten months later when a drift was being driven to cut as much coal as possible. Then troubles began to appear and by October 1786 only four or five men were at work because of flooding in the pit. In the year ending 30 September 1786 only £31 freeshare was paid.

Jacob Mogg held his interest in the mine for a long time, and, in partnership with John and Ralph Gaby, he took a new lease for 31 years from 12 February 1799. He died soon afterwards, as did Richard, his illegitimate son, in 1829. John Gaby's share went to his son Stephen, while Ralph willed his share to Walter Gaby, who became a lunatic. In 1830, two-thirds of the shares were held by the Mogg trustees, one-sixth by Sarah Gaby, and one-sixth by Charles Hollwey, who had purchased his holding from the Gaby family. In view of the deaths of most of the partners, the mine was in a very poor state and the lease, on its expiry in 1830, was not renewed.

During this period of ownership the pit had been entirely closed, only to be reopened about 1812.

The mine was restarted soon after 1830 by the same partners; however, in the winter of 1833-4, excessive rain flooded the pit and stopped work for three months. The lessees claimed a reduction of freeshare to compensate for the expenses in erecting 'powerful Engines and Machinery' to drain the pit.

On 13 May 1846, Hollwey and Sarah Gaby, together with James Perrin and Joseph Cook, signed a lease from 30 August 1845; they had, however, been landing coal in May 1845. A condition of the lease was that the engine shaft would be deepened within four years and that comprehensive exploration of the area would be carried out.

Charles Hollwey was the dominant shareholder in the pit throughout the middle years of the century but his heavy involvement in other collieries—Clandown, Welton, etc—caused him to decline a new lease when the 1846 lease expired in 1877. On 25 October 1882, William B. Beauchamp and Theophilus Gullick obtained the lease for a term of 31 years from 30 August 1880, having begun negotiations with the Duchy over a year previously. After Beauchamp's death in 1894, his son Frank took over the pit. Ownership was in the hands of the Farrington Collieries Co, though the names Radstock Coal & Wagon Co and Radstock Coal Co were used for certain aspects of the concern. By 1904, Frank and Louis B. Beauchamp owned the Farrington company jointly, holding equal shares.[4]

It was under the Beauchamp family that serious modernisation was begun. In 1897 the shaft was deepened, proving the Jubilee, 15 Inch and 21 Inch seams, all of which were, in later years, mined in considerable quantities to the rise of the shaft. Possibly the most significant single development was the construction of a siding from the pit to the B & NSR; though planned by Charles Hollwey, the execution was Beauchamp's.

Under an agreement dated 15 February 1871 the pit was intended to be connected with the B & NSR, a plan of this date showing the land that would be needed for the siding connection. The B & NSR had agreed to lay down such a siding for the colliery in return for concessions made when building their main line from Bristol to Radstock, and on 11 August 1875 the contracting firm of Saunders & Ward agreed to undertake the work. However, the siding was not in fact laid until 1882; a plan dated 8 August 1882 shows the proposed siding, and the necessary slewing of the main line so that the siding could run parallel to it and form a junction with the Old Mills Colliery sidings. For the privilege of using the Old Mills junction, the Radstock Coal & Wagon Co paid £250 to Old Mills, this being a proportion of the £1,000 that the junction had originally cost. Additionally, Farrington contributed a proportion of the annual maintenance costs of the junction.

At least three locomotives are known to have been used at Farrington to work the siding, a slightly odd state of affairs when one considers that this was a relatively small colliery. One locomotive is believed to have arrived about 1902 and was an 0-4-0 saddle tank with outside cylinders, built by Beyer Peacock of Manchester (works number 1736). It was supplied new to Meakin & Dean on 3 September 1877 and probably worked on the construction of Blagdon Reservoir in Somerset. No positive evidence of this locomotive's history is available until August 1904, when the Avonside Engine Company at Bristol sent spares to Farrington for it.[5] Before this, possibly when it was sold from Blagdon, the locomotive had been rebuilt with a new Avonside boiler at the Avonside company's works. It may be that this locomotive arrived by 1885; for in the year to August 1885, 25,912 tons of coal were despatched by rail, the cost of locomotive haulage and maintenance being £426.

The chronological order of the locomotives is unknown but what is believed to have been the next locomotive (there was only one at the colliery at any one time) was built by Pecketts of Bristol (works number 520). It was their type R1, working at 140psi and despatched new to the Millbrook Iron & Steel Co in South Wales on 8 June 1891. It later passed to a contractor named G. Palmer and subsequently arrived at the colliery. After a period at Farrington, it was transferred to another Beauchamp company, East Bristol Collieries Limited, returning to Somerset in later years at Beauchamp's Norton Hill Colliery.

The third and last locomotive was another 0 – 4 – 0 saddle tank, built by Bagnall of Stafford. Nothing is known about the locomotive, though it may have been named *Grazebrook*. After closure of the colliery, the Bagnall was advertised for sale on 9 December 1921 and again on 7 July 1922; but its final disposal is not known.[6]

The duty of the locomotives was to shunt the pithead and work trains of two or three wagons to and from Old Mills siding. When the locomotive broke down, horses had to be hired from a timber merchant in Midsomer Norton. One horse could pull an empty wagon as far as the curve by the GWR,

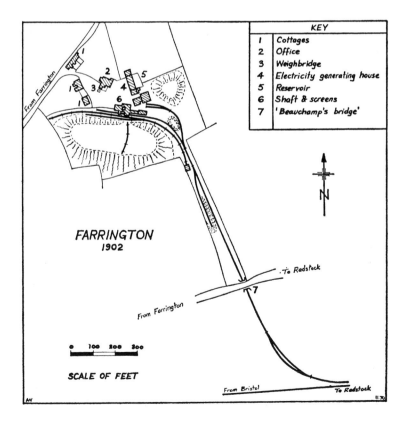

KEY

1	Cottages
2	Office
3	Weighbridge
4	Electricity generating house
5	Reservoir
6	Shaft & screens
7	'Beauchamp's bridge'

FARRINGTON
1902

SCALE OF FEET

but then all the horses had to be hitched on to each wagon in turn in order to surmount the gradient up to the pithead. This method of working was presumably in force before Farrington obtained a locomotive.

The surface layout of the pit at the turn of the century was fairly conventional, except that it had a large electricity generating station, the use of electricity so early in the twentieth century being unusual in Somerset.

Farrington was strike-bound during the 1921 dispute, as were most pits in Somerset. Sir Frank Beauchamp, on 7 February 1921, informed the Somerset Miners' Association that he had finally decided to close the pit, probably at the end of March. To the employees he gave the warning that unless the men returned to work immediately, he would close the pit. The men did not return to work and Beauchamp implemented his decision, the pit ceasing work on 31 March 1921. However, a limited reopening occurred and the pit was not finally closed until October 1921; after the failure of a reopening scheme, machinery was salvaged and the plans of abandonment of the colliery were dated 4 August 1922.

> The reason given for the closing of the pits is the fall in coal prices and consequent unprofitable working. The outlook for the Somerset Coalfield appears to be very bad, and it was stated at the County Council meeting that there is considerable distress in the district.[7]

Present-day remains are quite numerous. The foundations of most of the buildings are still visible, including those of the winding engine. About a third of the electric power house remains standing, and is used as a hay barn, while the former colliery offices look virtually unchanged in their new role as dwelling houses. The capped shaft of the coaling pit, with an iron inspection pipe therein, can be clearly seen, as can most of the railway track bed, including one parapet of the bridge (known as Beauchamp's Bridge) under the main road. In fact the main casualty has been the tip, which has been in great part dug away for road foundations. During the first week of August 1970 the track bed of the railway between the bridge and the GWR was levelled and sown with grass.

Page 137 Lower Writhlington Colliery: *(above)* viewed from the hillside below Braysdown Colliery c 1900. From left to right: Cornish engine house; winding engine house; head-gear and screens; Evans' foundry; *(below)* the pithead in 1969

Page 138 (above) The Foxcote carting boys in 1904; (below) Kilmersdon Colliery prior to demolition of the two chimneys

OLD MILLS AND SPRINGFIELD COLLIERIES

These two collieries, originally worked as separate units, became grouped as the Old Mills Colliery of the National Coal Board. Because of this there is often some confusion as to their names, the pit commonly referred to as Old Mills being, in fact, Springfield.

Old Mills was the first of the two pits to be sunk, work beginning about 1860. The instigators of the venture were Messrs Pooll, Evans & Hill, who became popularly known as the Old Mills Company. One of the partners, William Evans, was the owner of that most famous Somerset ironworks, Paulton Foundry, sited just to the north of Old Mills. The concern grew up, and thrived with, the local coalmining industry, and Evans' connections with the two concerns ensured that the foundry obtained the contracts for equipping the new pit. The foundry was not only concerned with wood and metal work, but also acted as coal factor and general haulier. Throughout 1861 and 1862 many orders came for hauling stone from Temple Cloud; freestone from Combe Down quarries near Bath; and lime, ashes and timber, all of which were needed for the construction of the surface works and for sinking the shaft.[8]

The actual sinking probably began in 1861; on 17 June, six plumb bobs were delivered, in order to check that the sinking was proceeding vertically. Coal was worked for some years before the shaft reached its full depth. The first recorded consignment of coal, 12 tons, left the colliery for Radstock on 3 September 1864. On 30 May 1867, the first customer is named, Wells Asylum, which purchased 95 tons of coal.

The second colliery, Springfield, is said to have been sunk after 1872 and completed in 1874, the reason for sinking being legislation making two shafts compulsory.[9] However, these dates are inaccurate. The lease of 'Spring Ground' was signed on 10 June 1867, giving Evans immediate possession of the ground in order to begin sinking, and also granting him an option to buy land for a railway siding in the event of completion of the B & NSR. Springfield pithead had a cast-iron plaque carrying the date 1868, suggesting that work began in that year.

J

The Springfield shaft cost £7 2s per fathom to sink, the men receiving 2s 6d for an eight-hour shift.[10] After the sinking had reached 300ft they also received a bonus of £40 to be shared between them. No pumping engine was installed, the Old Mills engine doing this work, while the winding engine was virtually a duplicate of that at Old Mills, with 26in x 60in cylinders.

Railway sidings were laid in almost immediately (the agreement being signed on 5 June 1874) at a cost of £1,000. Another agreement (8 August 1882) allowed Farrington Colliery to make a junction with the Springfield siding, after which the layout remained substantially unaltered.

Ownership of the collieries was more or less unchanged from their opening, under the Old Mills Colliery Co. On 1 July 1931 the firm of William Evans & Co (Old Mills Collieries) Ltd was formed to acquire the interests in the pits, the directors being Messrs Redmayne, Allott and Kemp-Welch, and in 1938 the company was merged with Mells Colliery. The Evans family had no interests in the pit, the title being chosen mainly to retain goodwill.

The new owners promptly set about considerable modernisation. The first coal-cutting machine was installed about 1935, though it was later removed. All the old boilers were replaced by six Lancashire boilers (three at each pit), and the beam engine was scrapped in favour of electric pumps. All the wooden tubs, of which there were 390 in 1938, were replaced by 400 tubs with mild steel bodies.[11] In October 1940 a Ruston & Hornsby $7\frac{1}{2}$ ton diesel locomotive replaced horses in the railway sidings, which had to be strengthened and improved.[12]

Old Mills shaft was steadily run down. In 1930, the output was 426 tons per week at Old Mills and 1,447 tons at Springfield and the disparity increased. In 1924 and 1932, Springfield had about 170 men at work, but the Old Mills workforce declined from 100 to 60 in this period. In October 1941 the shaft ceased coal winding and was thereafter retained as upcast, and for materials, men and emergency use. The self-acting incline down which tubs had been run to Springfield screens had earlier been replaced by an engine-worked line, with the eng-

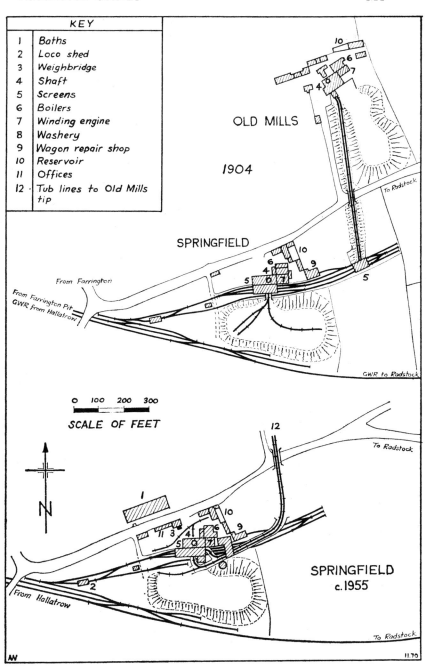

KEY

1	Baths
2	Loco shed
3	Weighbridge
4	Shaft
5	Screens
6	Boilers
7	Winding engine
8	Washery
9	Wagon repair shop
10	Reservoir
11	Offices
12	Tub lines to Old Mills tip

OLD MILLS

1904

To Radstock

SPRINGFIELD

From Farrington

From Farrington Pit
GWR from Hallatrow

GWR to Radstock

0   100   200   300

SCALE OF FEET

N

12

To Radstock

SPRINGFIELD
c.1955

From Hallatrow

To Radstock

To Radstock

AW   11.70

ine sited at Old Mills. After the closure, the engine and endless rope system was installed at Springfield, where it pulled
tubs of dirt up to the tip at Old Mills.

During 1944 a Sirocco fan was installed at Old Mills, replacing the furnace ventilation that was the last to operate in
Somerset. Finally, a Baum coal-washing plant was brought into
use at Springfield in October 1945 at a cost of £23,500.[13] All
this had significantly helped output; in the eight years before
nationalisation an average of 75,047 tons pa had been wound,
yielding an average profit of £21,556pa.

Under the National Coal Board modernisation was continued. In 1963, the steam winder at Springfield was replaced by
a 350hp electric winder that had been lying in store at Cwm-
llynfell Colliery in South Wales. This was associated with the
introduction of coal ploughs in April 1962, which doubled
output-per-man-shift. After nationalisation, utilisation of the
washery had been increased when coal from Pensford was
brought down the North Somerset line for washing. Bottom-
door hopper wagons were obtained for this traffic and the layout of the sidings was altered; however, this traffic ceased in
1958 and the washery was closed about 1962, as there was no
market for washed coal. The opportunity was then taken to
introduce new tub-tipping equipment and build new screens,
while the old tublines out to Old Mills tip were removed and
lorries substituted for dirt carriage. Finally, new tubs were
again introduced, this time with a capacity of 15-16cwt. Another Ruston locomotive, of 88hp, was brought to the sidings
and the first was transferred to Kilmersdon Colliery.

Despite all this, the pit was closed on 1 April 1966 to provide
men for the remaining collieries. Salvage was finished in
October 1966, after which both shafts were filled with dirt.
Dawson of Clutton felled Springfield chimney in March 1967
and the scrap metal at both pits was removed. In June 1969
Springfield site was entirely demolished (except for the winding house) and levelled with colliery dirt; it is now used as a
contractor's depot. Similar demolition was begun at Old Mills
in July 1970, the winding engine here having been removed
to the Bristol City Museum for preservation. The most prom-

inent feature of the colliery, the 150ft conical dirt tip, seems likely to survive for some while.

CHURCH FIELD COLLIERY

Otherwise known as Farrington or Ruett Slant, the latter name recalling some of the early pits in the area, this small winning was conceived by a group of miners who lost their jobs on the closure of Farrington Colliery in 1921. Men were recruited until there were about twenty willing hands and two drifts were begun in a field near Farrington Halt on the GWR North Somerset line. The lease was granted to the Farrington Gurney Coal Co Ltd by the Duchy of Cornwall on 1 January 1922 and all dues were waived until such time as the pit could afford to pay them.[14]

Work on the drifts began late in 1921, the first sod being cut by George Dowling, and about a year later the Middle Vein had been proved and coal was being won, often from pillars of coal left by old workings. There was a stationary haulage engine and boiler, brought from the closed Burchells level at Clutton. It was a small-scale enterprise, for the mine had only about ten wooden tubs, and that there were never more than about twenty men working there.

Potential danger from the nearby flooded workings of Farrington Colliery caused the mine to be closed in 1923, and the men began to look for a new site. With the help of the Duchy, work began on another pair of drifts at nearby Marsh Lane.

MARSH LANE COLLIERY

Once the site had been settled, machinery was transferred from Ruett and seventeen men started work on driving the two drifts. Work began about May 1924 and was finished by July 1927. A new company, Marsh Lane Collieries (Farrington Gurney) Ltd, was registered on 1 July 1927, its stated object being to enter into a 21-year-lease with the Duchy from 1 January 1924 to work 'the Jubilee Series of Seams remaining ungotton in the rise . . . of the now closed Farrington Colliery Winding Pit, approximately 80 acres in extent. . .'

The company's capital was £4,000, divided into 800 £5

shares and it was a condition that no workman aged 18 or over could be employed unless he first bought a share; on 4 August 1927 there were twenty-nine shareholders.[15] The fact that the miners were also shareholders appears to have created problems for the Somerset Miners' Association. In the 1926 strike, the Marsh Lane men were deemed to be outside union jurisdiction and could not, therefore, be prevented from working, though only 8-9 tons of coal were then being produced each day. On 1 January 1932 a group of men applied to join the union but were refused since they were also shareholders.[16] One can imagine a debate about whether the owners could unfairly treat the workmen when both groups consisted of the same people! By 1944, workers who were not shareholders had been allowed to join the union and, shortly after, shareholders also were admitted.[17] Strikes, not surprisingly, were unknown at Marsh Lane, where the miners were the first in Somerset to receive holidays with pay.

Coal was sold at the pithead to local customers or taken to such places as Cheddar and Glastonbury in the pit's two motor lorries. The colliery plant was on a slightly more lavish scale than at Church Field, the single boiler having a tall metal chimney. Ventilation was unusual—and economical—in that the air passed through the workings of its own accord.

One moment of distinction came on 7 July 1934, when the then Prince of Wales visited the pit and went underground in one of the coal tubs.[18] It is remembered that washing arrangements were non-existent and the Prince had to be supplied with soap and towels by one of the miner's wives.

Several exploratory works were undertaken, a borehole being put down by contractors. This proved the Rudge Seam at the base of the Trias, but its thickness was not definitely known. An exploratory drivage was begun, dipping from the 21 Inch Seam but, after driving 570ft, water-bearing sandstone was encountered and work had to cease until a pump had been obtained. The water was removed, a level crossmeasure drift was begun and the Rudge was proved at the end of 1946. Mining immediately started, and the drivage was continued until 16 May 1948 by the NCB.

The Rudge was worked until the pit's closure on 4 November 1949 due to exhaustion of reserves in the 21 Inch. Because there was only one connection to the Rudge workings only a few men were allowed to work there, and the cost of a second connection was thought too great. On closure, most of the 45-50 employees were transferred to Old Mills Colliery, and the private company was wound up on 11 March 1955. It may be mentioned that Marsh Lane was the last pit in Somerset to use the guss and crook, in conjunction with putts, for regular coal working.

Today, few traces are visible other than the grass-covered waste heap and the explosives store room. The drift mouths have been filled in and can only be located with difficulty.

Notes begin on page 268.

9 THE DUCHY MINES

Around Midsomer Norton the minerals were largely the property of the Duchy of Cornwall and the influence of this owner on the development of mining there was very marked. The coal was worked by three main collieries—Old Welton, Clandown, and Welton Hill—each pit mining under leases covering about a third of the area. There were also some earlier pits, which can be briefly mentioned first.

In 1750 Welton had two pits, but the first major lease was taken by John and Jacob Mogg, George Hodges, Thomas and John Bush, William Savage and James Moore on 27 April 1756.[1] They sank several pits, which became quite profitable, landing about £100 worth of coal each month. On 14 January 1757 they obtained permission to sink shafts at Welton Farm.[2]

John Bush, Hodges and Moore had died by 1774 when an extension of the lease was granted to 1805. After 1777, however, the pits became less profitable and several partners dropped out. The remaining partners took a new lease on 16 July 1790[3] and in 1808 the shares were as follows:

Representatives of Jacob Mogg	2/14
Representatives of John Mogg	2/14
Representatives of George Hodges	2/14
James Savage	3/14
William Kelson	3/14
John Paget	2/14

In addition to these partners, James Tooker & Co had mines in the area in 1783, though the exact locations of most of these are unknown. The Mogg's Welton Farm Pit was 270ft deep

with waterwheels for pumping. Jeanes Pit, beside the Farrington – Welton road, was then being put into order. The Welton
Farm Pit may have been known as Eastern Pit, Western Pit
being an alternative name for Jeanes. There were also Shock's
Pit and Orchard Pit, the former being 387ft deep. In 1782, the
produce of all these various mines was worth £1,900pa.

In more recent times, G. H. Thatcher owned the Welton
Bridge Colliery.[4] Work stopped there in 1887 and it closed
soon afterwards. In 1893 Thatcher sank a trial pit down to the
Slyving Vein, but this never came into production.

OLD WELTON COLLIERY

This colliery was opened by about 1783. It used waterwheels
for pumping, and in 1798 a new wheel was erected to draw
coal up the shaft, which system had the advantage that fuel
consumption, 'as in the new way by the steam engine', was
altogether avoided.[5] The earliest certain mention of the pit's
owners was in 1802 when Joseph House bought a share. The
Mogg and Rees-Mogg families bought shares in 1841, 1849,
1854, 1856 and 1858, becoming the major shareholders. Between 1842 and 1863, John Rees-Mogg received £700 in dividends. He took a new lease of the colliery on 30 April 1846,
together with John Moore Paget and Thomas Savage.

No details of the colliery plant or any facet of its operations
have survived, other than the fact that coal sales in the year
ending September 1821 totalled £9,621. In the year to 23 May
1846, 13,838 tons of coal were raised, and dividends totalling
£11,500 were paid between 1851 and 1857. After this date,
conditions deteriorated and only two dividends were paid up
to 1863. There was no improvement up to 1876 when the
partners despaired and did not renew the lease.

However, the pit was not closed. During the 1870s, William
Beauchamp and Theophilus Gullick started to buy Old Welton coal for their newly founded coal-factoring business and in
1876 bought shares in the colliery. On 22 October 1878 they
signed a new lease and continued working the pit under the
title of the Old Welton Colliery Co.[6]

The new owners had considerable ambitions for modern-

ising the colliery, for which there was certainly great scope. In
1885, James McMurtrie had valued the entire undertaking at
only £2,733. Beauchamp decided to deepen the northern shaft
to get to the Farrington Series, and this work was carried out
in 1886-8 at a cost of £2,115. To supply materials for the sinking, Beauchamp revived the Old Welton brickworks, near the
colliery, in 1886; but as a commercial venture it was unsuccessful, producing very poor quality bricks.

Concurrent with this expenditure was an improvement in
the colliery's rail communications. The SCC tramroad served
the pit but, after the B & NSR arrived in Radstock, proved
unsatisfactory. It cost 1s 4d per ton to cart coal to Radstock,
plus a 5½d toll to the SCC, and the tolls due to the Waldegrave
family for the use of their tramroad totalled £12 8s 0d in 1870.[7]
Beauchamp decided to obtain a standard-gauge siding but ran
into difficulties. The SCC tramroads were then owned by the
S & D but the nearest railway to Old Welton was the GWR,
only 100yd away. The S & D failed to come to any arrangement with the GWR, and in February 1885 decided to see
Beauchamp about laying a siding themselves, presumably
along the course of the tramroad. Beauchamp, however, had
got fed up with waiting and made his own agreement with the
GWR for the construction of the siding. Earthworks were laid
down on the tramroad to make the connection.

The S & D were naturally upset to find that their traffic
from Old Welton had ended and were even more annoyed
when they discovered the reason. There was, however, very
little they could do; they noted the illegality in an agreement
of 6 April 1886, but allowed that the 'interference' could remain. They also demanded a 'yearly acknowledgement' of 10s
to compensate for the loss of traffic.

The expenditure on the shaft, the siding, and other new
plant, nearly bankrupted the pit. After 1886, only two profits
were made: £597 in 1886 itself, and £399 in 1894. Losses
amounted to £17,429 and, in or about August 1896, the
colliery was closed.

It must surely have been obvious then that Old Welton was
worthless as a production unit; nonetheless, F. J. Bird of Clan-

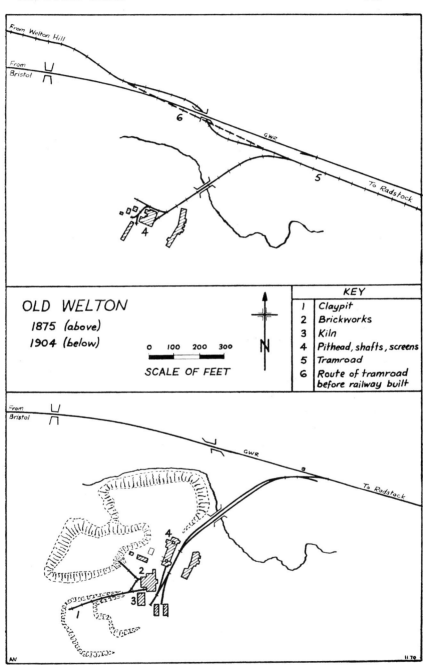

From Welton Hill

From Bristol

6

GWR

5

To Radstock

4

OLD WELTON

1875 (above)
1904 (below)

N

0   100   200   300

SCALE OF FEET

KEY	
1	Claypit
2	Brickworks
3	Kiln
4	Pithead, shafts, screens
5	Tramroad
6	Route of tramroad before railway built

From Bristol

GWR

To Radstock

4

2

3

1

AN   11.70

down Colliery took a lease on 31 March 1897. By May 1901 he
had repaired the winding shaft but mining had not been resumed. It never was. In January 1923, John Iles of Clandown
proposed to develop the colliery but found that the Government was not prepared to lend the necessary money. Finally,
Sir Frank Beauchamp acquired the colliery and brickworks on
5 May 1927 with the object of increasing the coal reserves for
Norton Hill Colliery. The Old Welton deep shaft was refurbished and brought into use as a ventilation and escape shaft.[8]

After Norton Hill closed in 1966 the machinery at Old
Welton was removed and the shaft filled up. The last landmark, the 60ft high brickworks chimney, was demolished on
9 December 1967, and the only remains are the SCC bridge
over the river and the retaining wall of the heapstead.

CLANDOWN COLLIERY

This colliery is first mentioned in 1793, when it is described
as 'Clandown New Coal Work'.[9] This refers to the projected
sinking, the lease not being signed until about 1801. The
adventurers were William Coxeter James; John, Elizabeth
and Julia Hill; Mary Langford; John Scobell; and a gentle-
man whose name has gone unrecorded. The site chosen for
sinking the shaft was, quite by chance, on the line of the north-
south fault that bisects the manor of Radstock and which has
at Clandown a vertical depth of no less than 720ft. The sinking was hard enough without the added problem of the fault,
which gave the partners the impression that no coal was to be
found, and on 8 November 1809 the work was abandoned.

By 1810, however, three of the partners had raised enough
money to restart the sinking; on 20 January 1810 an engine
was being erected at the pit and £2,000 had already been
spent. Finally, the reward came, around 24 November 1811,
when at the enormous depth of 1,200ft coal was found. Greatly
encouraged, the adventurers started work on sinking the engine shaft and a start was made on the erection of a second
engine. Some coal was wound up to 12 October 1812, by which
date the Duchy had received £15 18s 0d in freeshare payments;
but at a rate of one-tenth this represents only a very small out-

put. The first dividend was paid in 1815, a date often erron-
eously quoted as the date of sinking. The rapid success of the
pit thereafter can be judged from the fact that in the year to
September 1821 coal worth £12,252 was produced.

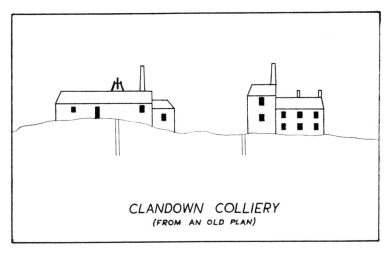

CLANDOWN COLLIERY
(FROM AN OLD PLAN)

Because of the fault, the shaft had been carried to a greater
depth than ever before in Somerset, finally reaching the Under
Little Vein at 1,437ft. In 1824, the pit was said to be capable
of raising 60-100 tons per day, due to 'improved machinery'.

On 30 April 1846 a new lease was taken by William Coxeter
James, Frederick Spry, John Scobell and John Hill, but lack
of capital caused this lease to be surrendered early, and on
19 October 1869 Charles Hollwey became the sole lessee. He
obviously made a success of the pit, for he took a new lease on
25 October 1882. He died in 1893 and the pit was operated by
his trustees for some years; but because of his death the lease
was surrendered several years early, on 14 December 1897.

By 1896, F. Bird of Norton House had shown interest in
acquiring the colliery, but he died in October 1897 before he
could take the lease and F. J. Bird became the lessor of Clandown, together with Old Welton and Welton Hill, on 31
March 1897. In May 1905 the Clandown Colliery Co became
a limited liability undertaking and by July 1906 Bird had sold
his shares to the company and become its chairman. The other

directors were George Batey (the colliery manager) and a Mr
Blake. Bird and his sisters were also the owners of F. Bird &
Co Ltd, coal factors, and all put a great deal of money into
Clandown, most of which they lost. Water was entering the
workings from the old Radford Colliery and the year ending
30 September 1907 showed a loss of £766. The following year
showed a worse loss, £1,143, and it was clear that the colliery
was unlikely to become a paying proposition.

It is surprising, therefore, that the colliery was not closed at
this period, and still more surprising that by 19 March 1917
John Henry Iles had become the sole proprietor.[10] Iles was
connected with a firm called Dreamland Margate, which appears to have operated amusement arcades at that South Coast
resort; his name occurs nowhere else in relation to collieries
and no one knows how he came to purchase Clandown. The
final owner was Sir Frank Beauchamp, who bought the pit in
December 1924 as a preliminary to his purchase of the Duchy
minerals as a whole.

The colliery was served by a branch off the SCC tramroad,
but after the GWR Frome – Radstock line was opened Clandown, in common with other collieries, made strenuous efforts
to send its coal by this line. The Waldegraves made available
—at a price—their tramway to the GWR but this did not find
favour at Clandown. The SCC toll was 5½d per ton and the
cost of carting 1s 8d per ton; consequently, by 1862, Clandown
had evolved an alternative mode of transport,[11] bringing

their coal to a siding by the Canal Company's Tramway and at
that point [they] slip their truck on to a travelling plat form
which is drawn by horses along a short road and after crossing
the turnpike enters the Great Western Railway Company's yard.[12]

Something must have gone wrong with this system, for by
1870 Hollwey was again using the SCC tramroad. In the week
ending 5 March 1870 about 250 'small wagons' were despatched, but, due to a toll of 3d per ton, arrangements were
being made to use the turnpike road again. By 17 March 1871
the new system was in use, coal going down the Clandown
tramway as far as the parish road, where it was transferred to
road vehicles.[13]

There was a long wait before a standard-gauge line was built to the colliery. A branch off the S & D was proposed in 1878 but, due to difficulties in fixing the tolls, the line was not opened until 18 September 1882. The tolls were fixed at 1½d per ton, the S & D working traffic to and from the foot of the incline up to the colliery.

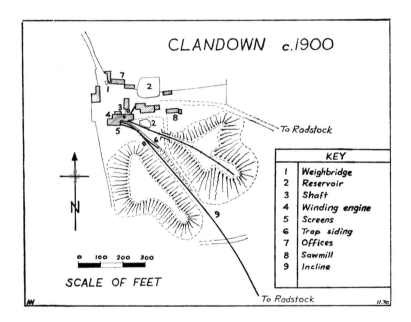

CLANDOWN c./900

To Radstock

KEY	
1	Weighbridge
2	Reservoir
3	Shaft
4	Winding engine
5	Screens
6	Trap siding
7	Offices
8	Sawmill
9	Incline

SCALE OF FEET

0   100   200   300

N

To Radstock

The Clandown colliers were a jolly lot, as they needed to be with the conditions of work as they were. The story is told of a group of miners walking to work and finding a drunk lying in the road. For a joke, they carried him to the colliery and took him underground, where, on sobering up, he was horrified to find himself in what he thought was hell! The conditions of work were indeed strict: underground, all coal had to be loaded by hand, for shovels tended to pick up dirt and a man would be fined if he was caught using one. In the year to 22 May 1846, 13,850 tons of coal were produced by this means. Somerset Collieries Ltd did very little modernising, though by 1925 an electric hauler had been introduced on the main

dipple. Additional boilers were installed, three being kept in
steam, with a fourth spare; but there was a chronic shortage of
tubs and the pit was thought generally unsuitable for mechanisation. On 24 August 1927 all the men were given a week's
notice, but closure of the pit was postponed eventually until
11 November 1929, after which the pithead was quickly demolished.[14]

Few traces remain today: the course of the incline is still
visible, as are the colliery offices. Around 1946 a breeze-block
factory was established on the colliery site, and in 1968, when
the firm was clearing an area for factory extensions, it un-
covered the old winding shaft lying dangerously in the middle
of the site. At the time of writing, the shaft is still visible.

WELTON HILL COLLIERY

This was the third and last of the Duchy collieries to be sunk
in the Welton area. The partners involved in Old Welton had
decided to sink a new pit, but, because of the multiplicity of
surface owners in the intended area, could not begin until
1812 when the legal problems had been settled. The lease was
signed on 8 February 1813 by William Kelson, William Coxeter James, William Savage, John Paget and Thomas Hollwey,
the last two holding one-eighth shares and the others quarter
shares each.[15] It was stipulated that the first work was to be a
'new and compleat Level Adit or Drain', followed by the
erection of a 'Fire Engine or Steam Engine' for drainage.

In accordance with the lease, work on the level began on
24 February 1813; the ground was very soft and gunpowder
was unnecessary. Sinking of at least one shaft followed and two
years later, in January 1815, the first coal was found at a depth
of 270ft. To celebrate the occasion the workmen were given a
free supper at the Greyhound Inn. The level met the shaft at a
depth of 111ft, but despite its aid there were still troubles with
water, for the pumps 'could scarcely stand for a month without
endangering the water running into the deep working'. The
completed shaft was 603ft deep and 6ft in diameter, two further shafts being sunk for pumping and ventilation.[16]

The colliery is noted as the second in Somerset to experi-

Page 155 A very
early view of
Huish Colliery
(c 1870?) show-
ing the beam
winding engine
and its solitary
boiler. Note
also the wooden
headgear and
single pulley
wheel

Page 156 Norton Hill Colliery: (above) c 1910. The bridge in the distance leads to the main dirt tip, while the smaller bridge over the sidings served a smaller tip; (below) the winding shaft in August 1965. Between the rails are the compressed-air rams for changing the tubs in the cages

ment with cage guides in the shaft: iron guides were introduced about 1840 but soon abandoned in favour of wooden guides, which were found to be very successful.[17] In these years the pit was quite profitable: up to 1850 a dividend of £1,000 was usual but after this the normal figure was about £800. Coke ovens were in use up to at least 1846, but were probably shut down soon afterwards. In the year to 23 May 1846, 10,746 tons of coal were raised.

On 30 April 1846 a new lease was signed. William James took no further part in the colliery's affairs and Thomas Hollwey, with his son Charles, were the main partners. Another lease was taken on 25 October 1882 by Richard Paget, William Rees-Mogg and Charles Hollwey, though Rees-Mogg doubted whether it was worthwhile.

The period after 1860 was a time of upheavals and alterations in which railways figured prominently. From its inception the colliery had been served by the SCC tramroad, a self-acting incline being needed to reach the pithead. This line was the longest branch off the Radstock tramroad and had the highest tolls—8d per ton, plus a carting cost of 1s 10d per ton.[18] In July 1878, after the opening of the B & NSR, the colliery applied for a siding at Midsomer Norton and Welton Station. The agreement was signed on 31 December 1879 whereby the colliery laid a narrow-gauge line from the pit to a new siding off the main line, and work was completed by June 1880 at a cost of £708. The narrow-gauge line was a self-acting incline down which the wooden colliery tubs were run to new screens erected on the siding. On 11 April 1888 plans were made to replace the narrow gauge by a direct standard-gauge connection, which would have saved an estimated £264pa, but the plan was not proceeded with.[19]

Modernisation, including overhaul of the beam pumping engine, was carried out in 1866-8, and ten years later the pit was raising an average of 20,000 tons pa. Up to 1884, however, there was a gradual decline in orders and a deterioration of the underground workings. During 1886, productivity improved somewhat, the colliery manager, Mr M. Shearn, reporting an average increase of 61½ tons of coal each week at a cost

K

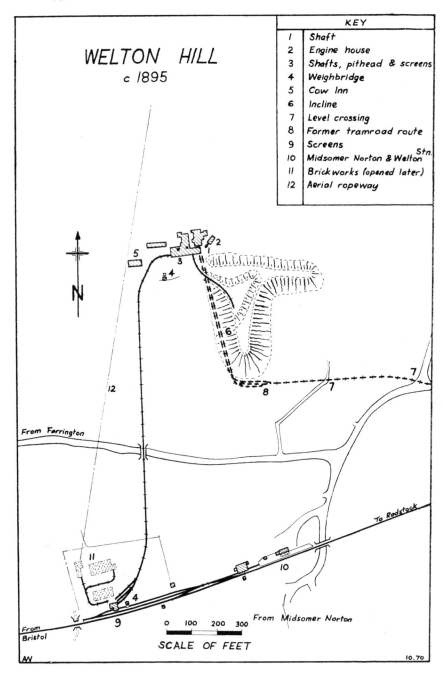

WELTON HILL
c 1895

KEY

1	Shaft
2	Engine house
3	Shafts, pithead & screens
4	Weighbridge
5	Cow Inn
6	Incline
7	Level crossing
8	Former tramroad route
9	Screens
10	Midsomer Norton & Welton Stn.
11	Brickworks (opened later)
12	Aerial ropeway

N

From Farrington

To Radstock

From Midsomer Norton

From Bristol

0 100 200 300

SCALE OF FEET

AN

10.70

of 5d per ton less than in 1885. Unfortunately, the selling price of the coal had decreased by 7¾d on the 1885 prices.

Much-needed development was considered and rejected. In June 1886 J. Batey had suggested deepening the shaft in order to work the Farrington seams, but on 27 June 1886 William Rees-Mogg wrote to Hollwey: [20] 'Most decidedly, I shall not have anything to do with sinking to the Farrington veins. My share of doing so would be about £5,000. . .'

The colliery was by now in such a poor state that the partners lost heart. Hollwey left to concentrate his money at Clandown and on 1 January 1889 William Beauchamp became the proprietor. At the takeover, the pit was valued at only £3,950. Beauchamp did little at Welton Hill, though it proved a useful training ground for his son Frank, who was taken on to the staff at a salary of £100pa. After William died in 1894, the pit was run by his executors.

After 1889 the financial picture grew worse, though the first three years showed a profit, due mainly to Beauchamp buying his own coal for resale by his Radstock Coal Co. The figures tell a sorry tale: [21]

Year	Profit (£)	Loss (£)	Wages (£)
1889	1,249	—	4,356
1890	1,736	—	5,455
1891	270	—	6,147
1892	—	322	5,899
1893	—	952	2,986
1894	—	576	3,255
1895	—	503	2,353
1896	—	555	1,524
1897	—	343	82

The colliery closed towards the end of 1896 and much of the plant was sold in the following year.

After 31 March 1897 the pit was taken over by F. J. Bird, under the grandiose title of Old Welton, Welton Hill & Clandown Amalgamated Collieries; Welton Hill was never reopened and in due course the pithead was demolished. The sites of all three shafts can be seen today, as can the routes of the narrow-gauge inclines to the GWR and the SCC tramroad, though the incline of the latter was tipped on after 1880. The house of the colliery manager at the pithead remains in use, but the weigh-house for road traffic is now derelict, as is the Cow Inn, which once provided refreshment for the miners as they left the pit.

Notes begin on page 268.

10 EARL WALDEGRAVE'S RADSTOCK COLLIERIES

Unquestionably the most famous Somerset colliery group in the nineteenth century was the Waldegrave family's Radstock Collieries. The family, Lords of the Manor of Radstock since the Civil War, was a relative latecomer into the coal-mining business for there was at first no suggestion that coal existed at Radstock. However, either on theoretical grounds or from guesswork, the idea arose that there might, indeed, be coal there and, on 12 May 1749, James Lansdown and others took a 42-year lease to explore the area. Fourteen years later, in 1763, coal was found at Old Pit (as it was later known) and the sceptics were confounded.

The 1749 lease was surrendered early and Lansdown, James Tooker and John James took a new lease on 29 September 1775. A new pit was begun (apparently Middle Pit) and coal was found in April 1779. John Smith was a managing partner in this work and stated, 'had it not been for me you certainley knows the coal never would have been found . . .' The cost was heavy, and Smith was forced to 'Mortgage [his estate] as deep as he can . . .' Sinking of the coaling pit was finished about March 1780 and, by April 1781, 'the coalwork equals expectation and has already sold nearly £2000 of coal'.

It was apparently at Middle Pit that the famous Hornblower pumping engine was erected. This engine had two cylinders (19in x 72in and 24in x 96in); in July 1782 the engine was 'not yet set going', while in October 1783: 'we are now got into a dispute with the Engineers about the payment for the Fire Engine as their demand far exceeds their Estimates'. Even after these troubles, the engine was not very successful, and was replaced within a few years.

In 1782, the sinking of Ludlows Pit was begun, and by 1783, when work stopped due to flooding, nearly £900 had been spent. Following the advice of a 'skilful person' the water was diverted and the pit completed about 1784. These three collieries proved to be immensely profitable; between 1804 and 1842, £153,450 was paid out in dividends. Two other important pits—Wellsway and Tyning—were sunk by nominally independent companies during this period, together with a rather minor work at Smallcombe. With the possible exception of the latter, all the pits were linked by tramroads.

In September 1840 the seventh Earl Waldegrave married Frances Elizabeth Anne, widow of John Waldegrave of Essex. The Earl died in 1846 and in 1847 the Dowager Countess married George Granville Harcourt, her third husband; and in this year legal proceedings were begun (possibly at Harcourt's suggestion) to remove the lessees of the pits and transfer full ownership to the Waldegraves. The proceedings were successful and, as from 31 December 1847, Lady Waldegrave obtained full possession. Following Harcourt's death, Lady Waldegrave took her fourth husband, Chichester, Lord Carlingford, in 1871.

After 1847 the collieries traded under the title 'Radstock Coal Co' until the style 'The Radstock Coalworks' was adopted about 1863. In 1868 or 1869, William Beachim (otherwise W. B. Beauchamp) commenced business under the title of the 'Radstock Coal Co'.[1] Not surprisingly, confusion arose, not least in the local post office, which frequently erred in delivering letters. Accordingly the Countess adopted a new title, 'Frances, Countess Waldegrave, Radstock Collieries', which was in use by September 1873. This did not solve matters and in 1878 the Countess went to the courts, seeking an injunction restraining Beauchamp from using a title that suggested he owned a colliery at Radstock, and judgement was given in her favour. It is curious that, in this action, the Countess was the plaintiff while Baron Carlingford, her husband, was the defendant.

Two famous names are associated with the Radstock Collieries—Greenwell and McMurtrie. George C. Greenwell came to Radstock as colliery manager after training in Durham; his salary was fixed in October 1853 at £500pa, plus a horse and gig, rent free house, free coal and grass for a cow. After 1858, he was also allocated 4 per cent of the profits of the collieries above £1,000. Greenwell was the discoverer of the Westbury iron ore field and went into partnership to develop it, much to Lady Waldegrave's displeasure.

James McMurtrie was born in Ayrshire and trained in Newcastle-upon-Tyne under Robert Simpson, manager at Radstock before Greenwell. In 1862 McMurtrie came to Somerset to manage the Newbury Collieries, but, shortly afterwards, Greenwell retired and McMurtrie took over at Radstock. In 1863 he also became agent to the Waldegrave estates and eventually took charge of most of the Waldegrave affairs. Among his many outside positions we can mention that he was secretary to the Somerset Coal Owners Association, Fellow of the Geological Society, chairman of the Great Western Colliery Co, director of Bath Stone Firms Ltd, and an alderman on the Somerset County Council. His importance to Radstock Collieries and to Somerset cannot be overestimated. In 1863, the collieries raised 111,000 tons of coal and made a profit of £5,936; in 1880, these figures had doubled. Between 1863 and 1881, a total of $2\frac{1}{2}$ million tons was raised and no less than £256,608 made in profit. McMurtrie retired in 1904, his son George becoming colliery manager and his son Hugh taking over the estates. He died on 2 February 1914.

The eighth Earl died at this time and for a while the pits were run by trustees, as they had been after the death of Lady Waldegrave in 1879. Gradually they lost their former importance and in 1919 it became necessary to sell part of the family estates. At the sale on 15 January 1920, Sir Frank Beauchamp was an important buyer. On 29 December 1925 Sir Frank obtained a licence to work Radstock Collieries from the ninth Earl, at a cost of £10,000.[2] Profits remained high under his ownership, at around £50,000pa up to 1934, although by then only Ludlows was in production. This pit finally closed in 1954 after a long period of uncertainty.

OLD PIT

Very little information on the early history of this colliery has survived. About 1804 a steam winding engine, built by a Mr Jeffries was erected, but it was poorly made and did not last long. In 1826 a Cornish beam engine was erected, and the pit was subsequently used to drain water from the other Radstock

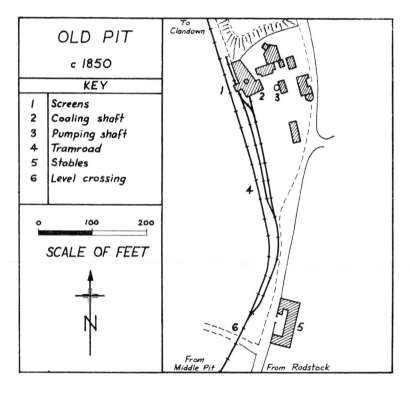

OLD PIT

c 1850

KEY

1	Screens
2	Coaling shaft
3	Pumping shaft
4	Tramroad
5	Stables
6	Level crossing

SCALE OF FEET

collieries. On 27 August 1853, seventy-two men were employed as follows:

Bailiffs	2	Deading men/boys	20
Breakers	19	Branchers	6
Carting boys	10	Door boys	1
Twin boys	10	Fill pits	2
Guss men	2		

The last recorded date of working at the pit was in the Under Little Vein in 1854, and this is almost certainly the date of closure for coal winding. At any rate, no men were working there by 29 May 1858. This was not the end, however, for the shaft continued to be used to pump water from the other Radstock pits until its replacement by the new Tyning pumps in 1872. In 1863 it was reported that a water drift from Ludlows was almost finished and all water except that from Tyning was being drawn at Old Pit.

Today very little remains to be seen. The shaft is covered with railway sleepers and hidden by dense undergrowth, and only the tree-covered batch is evident. The name of the pit is commemorated by Old Pit Terrace, a nearby row of former miners' cottages.

SMALLCOMBE

The first known coal lease relating to Smallcombe Colliery is dated 22 May 1797, when Robert Tudway and the Rev Richard Chaple Whalley leased all the coal under 32 acres of land to James Tooker, Francis Whalley, John Billingsley, John James the elder, Rev Henry Gould, Joseph Hill, Charles Savage, Simon Hill, Francis White, John James the younger, Richard Langford and Samuel Blacker.[3] In the following year articles of partnership were signed between the lessees and Richard Whalley, one of the two lessors, as the latter had decided to become a partner, and it was agreed that this co-partnership would be called the Smallcombe Coal Company. The pit was probably sunk in the same year.

By 1804 the pit was served by a tramroad branch from the line to Clandown Colliery. In 1819 'engines for drawing coal and water' are first mentioned at the pit. No details are known of the surface plant; in fact the only surviving record of the pithead is that on an old drawing of a section through the workings. The north western shaft was the winding shaft, the other being the pumping shaft.

On 31 December 1847 the Waldegrave family took over the working of the colliery from the partnership, but now the pit was nearing the end of its life, and in the twelve months ending 23 May 1846 only 6,067 tons of coal were landed, an average of about 120 tons per week.

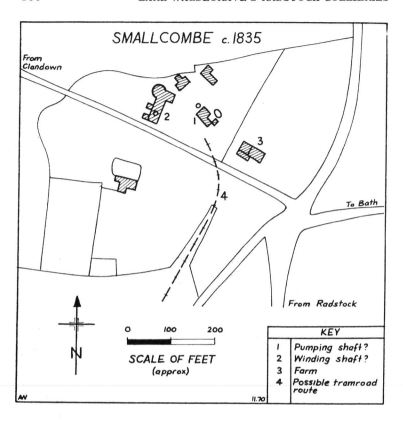

SMALLCOMBE c. 1835

From Clandown

To Bath

From Radstock

SCALE OF FEET
(approx)

N

KEY	
1	Pumping shaft?
2	Winding shaft?
3	Farm
4	Possible tramroad route

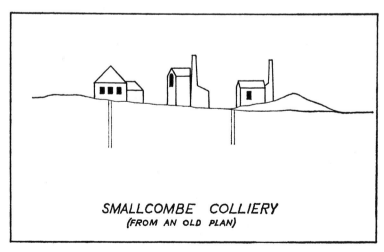

SMALLCOMBE COLLIERY
(FROM AN OLD PLAN)

The first underground survey was made on 17 March 1854, possibly to place on record the location of the workings before it was too late. On 17 May 1855, the Radstock Colliery letter book records: 'I am unable to say if the Smallcombe pit will be permanently abandoned; it is suspended for the present'. As it happened, the suspension was permanent, and the colliery was never worked again.

Very few traces remain today. Both shafts have been filled up, though the stonework at the top of the pumping shaft may still be found in a field. Nothing at all is to be seen of the buildings; the batch has become buried under later tippings from Clandown and the tramroad course is now a road.

MIDDLE PIT

As with Old Pit few details are known of the early history of Middle Pit. A steam pumping engine was erected in 1801, and in or about 1804 a steam winder was installed, the latter lasting for many years and increasing the output at the time of its installation from 20 to 50 tons per day. Originally, power had been provided by a 30ft waterwheel but this was superseded by the steam engines.

A cage was in use by October 1853, it being reported, 'the cage now in use at Middle Pit has three decks holding two boxes of coal per deck'. It was proposed to replace this by a four-deck cage holding four 2ft gauge trams.[4]

After February 1880 the idea of deepening Middle Pit to the Farrington Series was discussed; the cost of sinking the shaft a further 600ft was estimated at £2,813. Some rebuilding of the colliery took place in 1881-3, preparatory to the deepening, and this work included new screens.

On 12 April 1884 a tender by John Pratten & Company was accepted for deepening the shaft by 300ft at 12ft diameter initially, and finishing it to 10ft diameter. Work began on 8 May but on 7 June the contractors were dismissed, for some reason unspecified. The sinking eventually recommenced and during the operations three salt-water springs were encountered. For a short time the water pumped out from these springs was used in the colliery boilers, with unfortunate con-

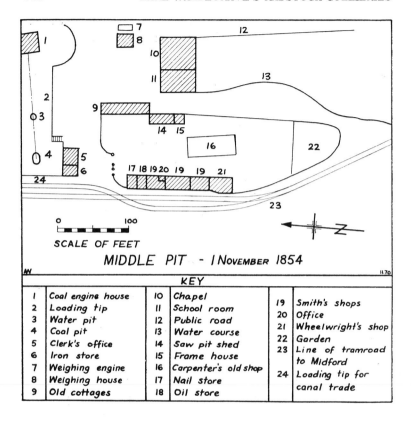

MIDDLE PIT - I NOVEMBER 1854

SCALE OF FEET

KEY						
1	Coal engine house	10	Chapel	19	Smith's shops	
2	Loading tip	11	School room	20	Office	
3	Water pit	12	Public road	21	Wheelwright's shop	
4	Coal pit	13	Water course	22	Garden	
5	Clerk's office	14	Saw pit shed	23	Line of tramroad to Midford	
6	Iron store	15	Frame house			
7	Weighing engine	16	Carpenter's old shop	24	Loading tip for canal trade	
8	Weighing house	17	Nail store			
9	Old cottages	18	Oil store			

sequences! The new shaft was brick-lined, with cast-iron tubbing in the watery strata where the first and second salt-water springs had been found.

The first seam of the Farrington Series was reached at a depth of 628ft below the original pit bottom, and on 25 January 1886 the sinking was completed at a total depth of 1,791ft. This made Middle Pit the deepest shaft in the Somerset coalfield, beating Braysdown by 51ft, a record that lasted until the deepening of the latter in 1911.

In 1886 McMurtrie reported on the sinking, stating that Ludlows would need deepening as well. He added that the existing Middle Pit engine was 'slow and antiquated' and needed replacement by a new 28in or 30in engine; and that three new boilers were also required, probably costing an additional £2,500, giving a total estimate of £6,762 for the entire work.

On 6 March 1896 McMurtrie wrote to Lord Waldegrave to say that Middle Pit had been abandoned for coal winding two years previously and the coal diverted to Ludlows. The colliery was reopened but during 1905 was again closed while extensive rebuilding operations were carried out. A new 120ft high chimney, a boiler house and a winding engine house were built. A new steel headgear, which is reputed to have come from Frongoch lead mine in Wales, replaced the old wooden one; the former engineer of Radstock collieries has recalled going to Wales to bring it back to Radstock, and stated that it took six weeks to dismantle. A hydraulic pump was installed at this time to replace the old method of raising water in tanks, and, while this was being done, the rubbish was taken underground to Ludlows pit. Upon the completion of the repairs to the shaft, 50-60 tons of coal per day were wound. A replacement winding engine (believed to have been built by the Wigan Coal & Iron Company) was obtained secondhand from Wiston Colliery, Huyton, and installed during the middle of 1906.

New screens were opened in October 1905. All the waste stone was sent back down to the pithead and put on the tramroad to go to Tyning. The old screens had chutes for loading the coal into the railway wagons; in those days stone was taken out at the working faces underground, and woe betide the unfortunate miner who had dirty coal! When the new screens were opened, nine or ten men and boys were employed to deal with the coal. A man and a youth unloaded the cages at the pithead, two men and three or four boys picked out the stone on the belts, and two checkweighers kept tally of the coal.

The pit continued to wind coal until the General Strike of 1926, when it was shut down on 30 April. On Monday 14 June the men were told to remove their tools from the pit, and, unless the dispute was settled by Wednesday, that the pit was to be dismantled. On Wednesday the men duly removed their tools, but the pit could not be dismantled as they refused to help with the work. Around October or November an unsuc-

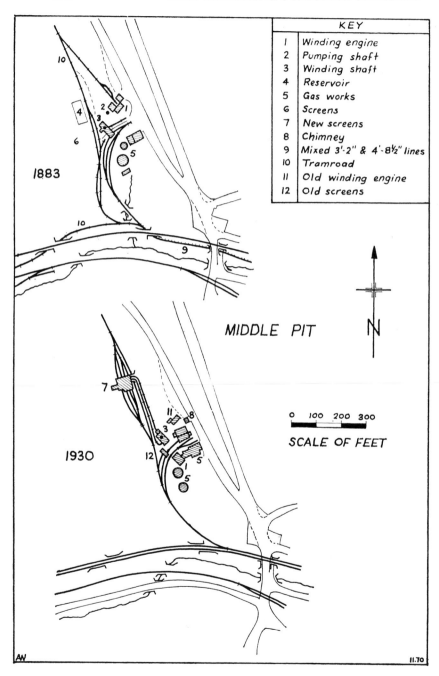

KEY

1	Winding engine
2	Pumping shaft
3	Winding shaft
4	Reservoir
5	Gas works
6	Screens
7	New screens
8	Chimney
9	Mixed 3'-2" & 4'-8½" lines
10	Tramroad
11	Old winding engine
12	Old screens

1883

MIDDLE PIT

N

1930

0   100   200   300

SCALE OF FEET

cessful attempt was made by a person or persons unknown to blow up the headgear. The explosive charges were laid but discovered before they could be detonated. After this, a police guard was mounted at the pithead.

Under Sir Frank Beauchamp's ownership, the pit survived for only a few years, being closed in June 1933. Many traces of the pit remain today, the 1905 winding engine house and the chimney being the major surviving structures. The sites of the original and the new screens are both visible, and many of the sidings are still in situ, together with the notice warning locomotives from entering the screen roads. The pithead retaining wall, capped shaft and course of the narrow-gauge incline up to the screens are also visible. The site is now occupied by the West Country Aluminium and Zinc Refining Company, which makes use of the remaining buildings.

LUDLOWS

Dirt from this pit was at first tipped on a small batch to its north-west, but this site soon became exhausted and, some time after the construction of Tyning incline, the dirt was taken there for disposal instead.

Up to 1850, man-riding was by 'hooker' attached to the chain in the shaft, but this system was superseded in that year, when the shaft was widened from 4ft 6in to 8ft diameter and equipped with wooden guides for two cages, which replaced the single cage formerly used.

Between 1858 and March 1863, the shaft was widened to 8ft in diameter as far as the Bull Vein, but remained in its narrow state for the rest of its depth; and a surface engine was erected with ropes down the shaft to work an engine plane underground.

On 3 November 1886, after the successful deepening of Middle Pit to the Lower Series, it was decided that Ludlows should be similarly treated. In February 1887 the specification (for deepening the shaft 600ft at 8ft finished diameter) was produced and in the following month Jasper Wylam signed an agreement to sink the pit at £5 10s 0d per fathom plus £2 per fathom for walling. The new sinking cut the first

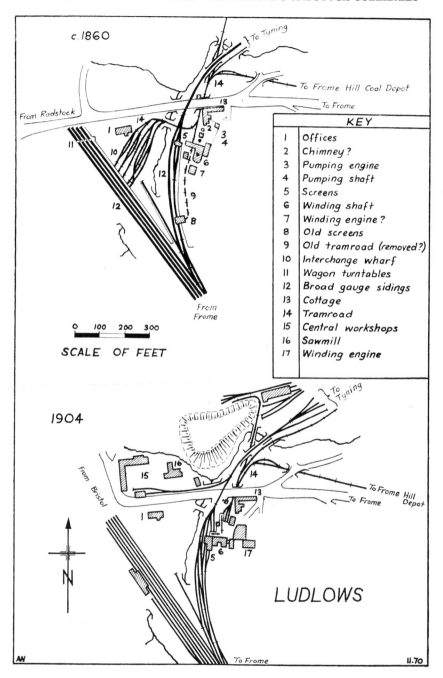

c.1860

To Tyning

To Frome Hill Coal Depot

To Frome

From Radstock

From Frome

	KEY
1	Offices
2	Chimney ?
3	Pumping engine
4	Pumping shaft
5	Screens
6	Winding shaft
7	Winding engine ?
8	Old screens
9	Old tramroad (removed?)
10	Interchange wharf
11	Wagon turntables
12	Broad gauge sidings
13	Cottage
14	Tramroad
15	Central workshops
16	Sawmill
17	Winding engine

0 100 200 300

SCALE OF FEET

1904

To Tyning

From Bristol

To Frome Hill Depot

To Frome

LUDLOWS

N

To Frome

11.70

coal on 10 March 1888; on 24 March it was agreed with Wylam to continue the work at an increased rate of £6 10s 0d per fathom. By 23 February 1893 a new winding engine and engine house had been erected at a cost of £1,880, £60 being recovered by the sale of the old engine.

In 1897 Wellsway was connected to Ludlows and the coal brought from the former was hauled from a landing about halfway up the Ludlows shaft. At this time, Ludlows was only working the deep seams, all the Radstock Series having been exhausted.

On 13 February 1926 an employee was killed while using the guss and crook, the first fatal accident since 1910. In evidence at the inquest, Alfred Milton, the examiner, said the men 'well use their guss . . . they like them like bread and cheese'. There followed a long discussion on the merits or otherwise of the guss; carting boys preferred it to other methods since it enabled them to perform their work with the minimum effort. George McMurtrie said that he had once tried to introduce straps instead of the ropes, but the men would not have them.

During the 1926 strike the engine house chimney was extended by 80ft to a height of 126ft. The work was executed by Harry Dawson of Clutton; and forty-three years later he was to demolish the chimney he helped to build! Other work carried out by Beauchamp during the strike was the replacement of the old wooden headgear by a steel headgear from one of his closed pits, and the construction of a new chimney for the power house. This second chimney was completed on 10 August and was 'an ugly looking object and built with his own bricks'.

After October 1930, mining was extended into the Clandown area and later, on 8 June 1936, permission was given to drive a branch towards the Welton area, subject to the provision of suitable dams. At 11.00am on 9 May 1934 a connection was made to Braysdown Colliery.

We can now consider the state of the colliery at nationalisation. The winding engine had two horizontal cylinders, each 30in x 60in, which ranked it among the largest in Somerset,

L

and a 14ft diameter drum. Underground, the first coal-cutter
had been put to work in November 1945, and by 1946, 64 per
cent of the output was so mined; and 900 tons of saleable coal
were being wound per week (ie about 45,000 tons per year),
which shows the continued drop in production since the 1930s.
It should be noted that the shaft capacity was over 1,500 tons
per week so the pit was only working at little over half its
capacity. Because of the long underground haulage distances
(there were over 11,000yd of 2ft gauge track underground) the
1947 report recommended that diesel locomotives should be
introduced, though this was never done. There were also modern pithead baths, opened on 30 May 1940. In June 1936 there
were about 375 men at the pit, but this total had fallen to 364
in November 1937 and further declined to 331 in 1947. The
report recognised that Ludlows was one of the poorer pits to
be acquired by the NCB, as there were reserves of coal to keep
the pit going for no more than about fifteen years, and many of
the coal-handling methods were archaic. The valuation of the
colliery at nationalisation was £118,687. After 1947 there was
a steady run-down on manpower until, by August 1953, only
214 men remained. That month, sixty were transferred to
other pits as the closure proposals were drawn up, and only
117 remained when the morning shift dug their last coal on
Friday, 19 March 1954.

The shaft was not immediately capped over because it was
kept in use as an upcast for Braysdown Colliery, and remained
as such until the latter closed a few years later. The pithead
baths are in use today for the miners from Writhlington.

Much of the surface is intact today, the engine house,
screens and bathhouse being the major surviving structures.
The 126ft high engine-house chimney remained in use by the
baths until January 1969, when it was demolished and replaced by a smaller aluminium chimney.

WELLSWAY

The lease for the sinking of Wellsway colliery was drawn up
on 31 December 1828, and was for a period of nineteen years.
Between 4 November 1829 and 20 November 1833 a sum of

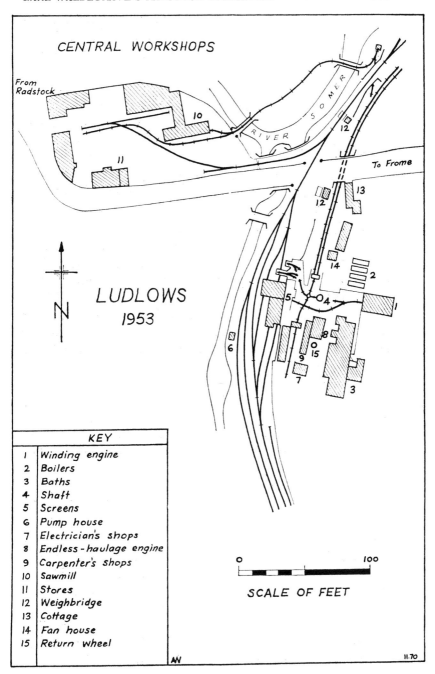

CENTRAL WORKSHOPS

From
Radstock

10

11

12

RIVER SOMER

To Frome

12

13

14

2

1

5

4

8

9 15

7

6

3

LUDLOWS
1953

N

KEY	
1	Winding engine
2	Boilers
3	Baths
4	Shaft
5	Screens
6	Pump house
7	Electrician's shops
8	Endless-haulage engine
9	Carpenter's shops
10	Sawmill
11	Stores
12	Weighbridge
13	Cottage
14	Fan house
15	Return wheel

0   100

SCALE OF FEET

11.70

£7,000 was subscribed to pay for the sinking. In 1839 a serious accident occurred. At that time a flat hemp rope was in use and in Midsomer Norton churchyard is a gravestone bearing the following legend:

> In this grave are deposited the remains of the twelve under-mentioned sufferers all of whom were killed at Wells Way Coal Works on 8th November 1839 by snapping of the rope as they were on the point of descending into the pit. The rope was generally believed to have been maliciously cut.

The stone was erected at the expense of the Wellsway coal-masters and was renewed in the summer of 1965 by the Somerset Miners Association.

In July 1854 cages were substituted for hudges, the former having four decks and carrying a maximum of ten men. About 100 men were employed here at this period. Between 1863 and 1865, £2,269 was spent on alterations. A new winding engine costing £300 was installed in April 1864, the old one being disposed of for £285. One engine wound both single shafts, and water was raised in tanks, this work being carried out by the night shift. The output for 1870 was over 20,000 tons, a figure which remained constant until 1911, when it began to decline.

A somewhat curious incident occurred on 10 April 1895 when one Alfred Dando, in an attempt to commit suicide, jumped down the shaft. Fortunately or unfortunately, he landed on top of the cage and lived to be tried for the act in a court of law.

In 1897 coal winding at Wellsway ceased. James McMurtrie wrote to the GWR on 25 December, after an interview with local railway officials, to say that the branch line to the pit was no longer needed because the coal had been exhausted and the pit was, therefore, uneconomic. McMurtrie's statement is a little curious, since the coal was *not* exhausted and the pit continued at work. The shafts, however, were now used only for men, materials and water winding, and the coal was taken on a very long and tortuous journey to Ludlows for winding. Wellsway retained its separate identity; its coal was recorded separately and the men were employed there rather than at

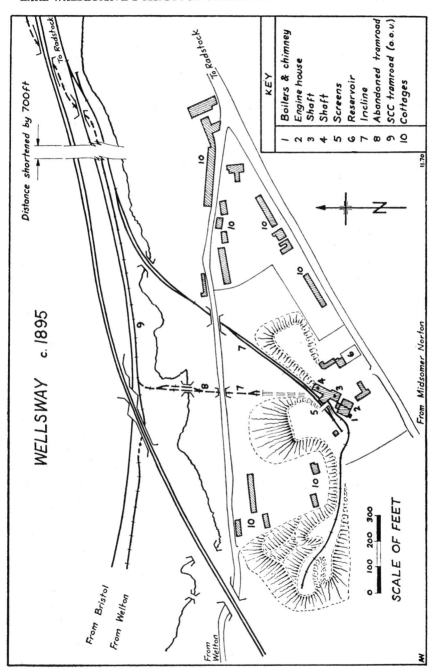

WELLSWAY c. 1895

KEY

1 Boilers & chimney
2 Engine house
3 Shaft
4 Shaft
5 Screens
6 Reservoir
7 Incline
8 Abandoned tramroad
9 SCC tramroad (a.o.u.)
10 Cottages

SCALE OF FEET

0   100   200   300

Distance shortened by 700ft

To Radstock

To Radstock

From Midsomer Norton

From Bristol

From Welton

From Welton

Ludlows. The new connection involved a 100yd incline and was altogether a most devious and expensive route to work.

About July 1899, an accident occurred.[5] The water in the sump of the shaft was used to condense steam from the surface engines and its normal temperature was about 190°F. It appears that there was a misunderstanding between the winding-engine man and the banksman, which resulted in the bottom deck of the cage being wound down into this water. Unfortunately there was a man on the bottom deck and he was scalded to death.

The pit worked quietly until 1920, when its peace was shattered and its affairs hit the headlines in the local papers. On 14 January the men reported to the union that they had strong reason to believe that the manager was trying to close the pit down and had applied to the Coal Controller for permission to do so.[6] This was indeed so, the obligatory sixty days' notice of closure being in fact due to expire on 14 February. On 6 February the *Somerset Guardian* reported that the men at Ludlows and Middle Pit had struck work in sympathy with three men who had been discharged from Wellsway, hoping to get them reinstated. The paper reported that 'at this time of the year the men [ie strikers] can find very little to occupy their leisure time, as it is rather too early for much work in the garden'. This strike lasted for eleven days, its end being due in part to a letter from the Coal Controller to the union saying that 'the Department had decided to direct the Owners to carry on the working of the pit' until there had been consultations between the owners and the men. The colliery company were further instructed not to stop any working places at the pit.[7]

A wordy battle in the correspondence columns of the *Somerset Guardian* now began. Mr McMurtrie explained that 'with Wells Way making a heavy loss, it was common sense to close that pit, in the hope of saving the two others'.[8] The men retorted by quoting an early statement of McMurtrie's that there was '30-40 years of working at the Wells Way pit'.

The truth was that the pit was in grave difficulties. The mining plans show the ridiculous methods of getting the coal away. Coal lying within a few hundred yards of Wellsway shaft had to be taken for nearly $\frac{3}{4}$ mile, with numerous interchanges, to reach the Ludlows shaft. Output was very low, only 229 tons for the week ending 25 February, and on average only 260 tons per week. Wages cost £1 14s 8d per ton of coal wound, resulting in a loss on sale of 18s 0d per ton. The employees, of whom there were over 100, attributed this loss to a shortage of basic equipment and deliberate neglect by the management. For example, no attempt had been made to work the Slyving Vein, 2ft 9in thick and of good quality, which could have greatly increased output. Wellsway was, incidentally, the last of the Radstock pits to work the Radstock Series, which was almost worked out in the Manor.

There were other reasons behind the pit's decline. Trouble was being experienced with machinery, notably the recently introduced coal-cutting machines, for on 12 February the cutting arms of both machines broke. One was repaired by 16 February but three days later the machine was buried when the roof fell on it. On 14 March the engine that provided power for the cutters broke down and was not repaired for a week. Only in the Great Vein, where there were six headings being driven by machine, were things going smoothly.

On 6 March 1920, a reprieve of three months was gained, to give the pit a chance to improve.[9] On 20 July, representatives of the union and the owners met the Coal Controller in London. After hearing of the continued serious losses that were incurred, the Controller gave permission for the pit to shut down after a period of six weeks had elapsed. It was hoped that about two-thirds of the men could be employed elsewhere. Another factor contributing to the closure was that, about this time, the winding-engineman had fallen asleep while winding up a full tank of water, and the tank and cage had rocketed out of the shaft, smashed part of the headgear, and had been drawn right up to the drum, stoving in one end of the engine house.

The pit eventually closed towards the end of August, and on 18 September 1920 it was stated that because of the closure, thirteen men were still out of work.[10] The pityard and incline sites were taken over by Sir Frank Beauchamp and later leased to Messrs Plummer & Hockey, a firm of joiners. The chimney was demolished about 1930 by Dawsons of Clutton and the headgear is said to have been blown down in a storm about 1932. The new owners of the site made good use of the northern shaft, tipping waste wood shavings down it. Up to about 1959 water could still be heard running at pit bottom, carrying the shavings to an unknown destination. Then the shavings proved too much for the water flow to cope with, and within a few weeks the shaft was filled with them. The southern shaft had been capped over in 1945 and now the other one was similarly sealed.

Substantial remains of the colliery buildings are to be seen today. The winding-engine house, weighbridge and stables remain, together with part of the sites of the tramroad and railway inclines.

TYNING

Tyning Colliery was sunk under leases of August and September 1837 by Samuel Palmer Blacker, John Collins, Jacob Collins, and Elijah Bush. It was the most easterly of the Radstock collieries, sited on the top of the north slope of the Somer Valley. In 1847 the colliery passed into the ownership of the Waldegraves, Countess Waldegrave paying £6,029 for the pit, including the 'tram carts'.

Up to 1872 the water from Middle Pit and Ludlows was raised at Old Pit, but because the rate of flow of the water had increased and the machinery at Old Pit was becoming worn, the winding engine there was required to raise water in tanks day and night, in addition to the pumps, to keep the pits dry. Wellsway was winding its water in tanks at night, and similarly Tyning, but because of the effects of a serious leak in the lining of the second shaft and an inrush of water from an adjacent colliery, Tyning was so inundated that the tanks could only prevent the pit from being completely drowned with great difficulty.

It became desirable, therefore, to adopt a central pumping

establishment and Tyning was selected because (a) it was the deepest shaft in the property; (b) it was nearest to the deeper part of the workings needing draining; (c) it was so situated that a system of waterways could be built at moderate cost; and (d) fuel was on the spot, which was not the case at Old Pit.

A new pumping engine was erected at Tyning in September 1873. It was built by Harvey & Co of Hayle in Cornwall; it had a 65in diameter cylinder, 9ft stroke, and the main beam was 30ft long and 5ft 3in deep in the centre. In January 1873 work had begun on enlarging the pumping shaft to 8ft diameter, the contractors being John Lewis, John Butt and partners. Great difficulties were experienced during the alterations as the shaft walling collapsed three times. A new shaft would have been better as things turned out, but the hazards were eventually overcome and the pumps were started about December 1876. Up to 24 December 1873 the alterations had cost £7,512, and the total cost eventually came to £17,234.

As if the troubles of widening the shaft were not enough, on 9 October 1876 a great quantity of water burst into the colliery from the Writhlington workings, causing considerable damage and drowning some men.[11] Some years previously the Writhlington company had reduced the 11yd barrier between their workings and Tyning to 5yd, which was the cause of the break-through. Work on pumping out the water began on 27 January 1877, and the Writhlington company were held liable for the damage. However, less than two years later, in July 1878, before the effects of the inrush had been fully dealt with, a second inundation, this time from the Old Woodborough pit (by then owned by Writhlington), poured into Tyning.

On 22 June 1905 the colliery was nearing the end of its useful life, for it was then working only two days per week, and in December 1907 it was said that the pit was 'very unsatisfactory'. By September 1908 it had deteriorated to the point where 'things could not be in a worse condition' and on 5 February 1909 the men had 'been at play . . . five days through water'. At the beginning of October, Lord Waldegrave was advised to close the pit as it had made losses of £162,

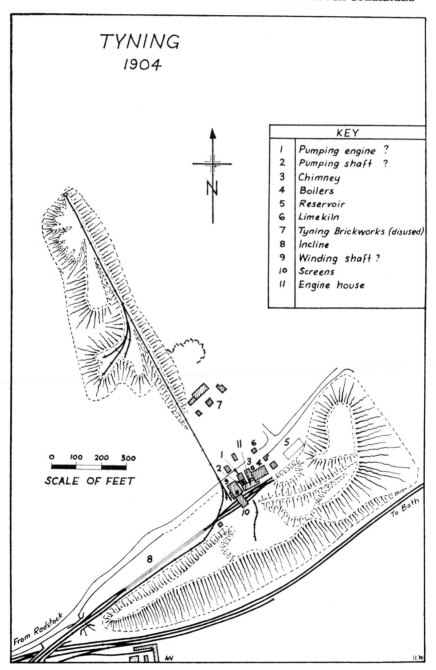

TYNING
1904

KEY

1	Pumping engine ?
2	Pumping shaft ?
3	Chimney
4	Boilers
5	Reservoir
6	Limekiln
7	Tyning Brickworks (disused)
8	Incline
9	Winding shaft ?
10	Screens
11	Engine house

N

0   100   200   300
SCALE OF FEET

To Bath

From Radstock

£232 and £300 in July, August and September respectively. On Thursday 11 November 1909, therefore, the pit was closed for coal winding; 354 tons had been produced in that month. All the men except three were found jobs in the other pits, the three being employed for a short time on dismantling work.[12]

The pit remained in use for some time afterwards for pumping. The Cornish engine was replaced by a Worthington-Simpson pump underground, and it is thought that the pit was finally abandoned in 1922.

The only activity at Tyning after 1922 was the tipping of dirt from Middle Pit and Ludlows (only Ludlows after June 1933) until the eventual closure of the latter in 1954. Today little remains to be seen of the pit itself, as the site has either been levelled, built over or tipped upon. However, as something like 2,500,000 tons of dirt have been tipped at the colliery over the years, the massive batches remain prominent landmarks on the hillside above Radstock.

RAILWAYS AT RADSTOCK

The passing of the Somersetshire Coal Canal Act in 1794 is the starting point for this section. The southern branch of the canal, from Radstock to Twinhoe Basin, was completed by 1804 but proved unsuccessful and by 1815 a 3ft 2in gauge tramroad had been laid along the canal towpath. Except for a period in August 1827, when a steam locomotive was tested, wagons were hauled by horses. As shown on the maps, branches off the tramroad served most of the collieries in the Radstock area. At some period between 1838 and 1848, the Waldegrave collieries established a central dirt-tipping area at Tyning, and a tramroad branch was laid to serve this.

In August 1844 the GWR proposed their broad-gauge Wiltshire & Somerset Railway, a scheme that underwent several changes before emerging as the Wilts Somerset & Weymouth Railway, with power to build a line from Frome to Radstock. This 8 mile railway was opened to mineral traffic on 14 November 1854.

An agreement dated 17 February 1853 made provision for

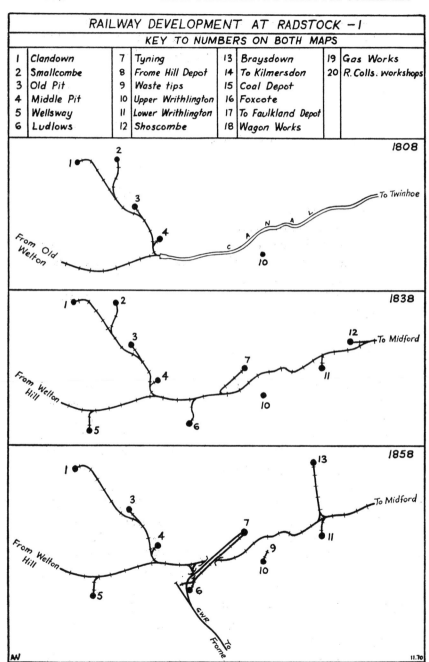

RAILWAY DEVELOPMENT AT RADSTOCK — 1

KEY TO NUMBERS ON BOTH MAPS

1	Clandown	7	Tyning	13	Braysdown	19	Gas Works
2	Smallcombe	8	Frome Hill Depot	14	To Kilmersdon	20	R. Colls. workshops
3	Old Pit	9	Waste tips	15	Coal Depot		
4	Middle Pit	10	Upper Writhlington	16	Foxcote		
5	Wellsway	11	Lower Writhlington	17	To Faulkland Depot		
6	Ludlows	12	Shoscombe	18	Wagon Works		

1808

From Old Welton

To Twinhoe

1838

From Welton Hill

To Midford

1858

From Welton Hill

To Midford

GWR To Frome

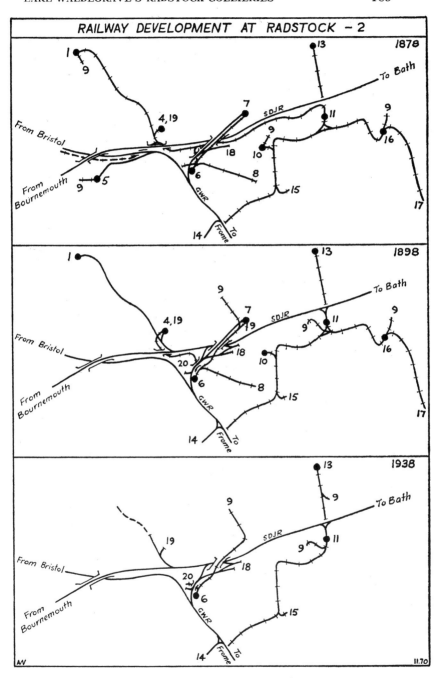

a siding off the WSWR to serve Ludlows Pit, construction beginning early in 1854. Four days after the opening of the
WSWR, the Radstock collieries decided to cease sending coal
along the SCC to Midford, though a remnant of this traffic
lingered on for some years. Other colliery owners also contemplated such a change and a meeting of these proprietors
decided, on 13 July 1854, to ask Countess Waldegrave for a
wayleave to pass over her land in order to load coal on the
broad gauge.[13] Terms were settled at an annual rent of £20 for
each proprietor, plus 6d royalty on each ton of coal carried in
excess of 1,000, and a minimum annual quantity of 1,800 tons.
To cope with this traffic, Lady Waldegrave laid a short tramroad branch from Ludlows to a tipping dock on the GWR.
She also suggested that the other owners might prefer an extension of the broad gauge rather than the tramroad; but they
denied this, nor did they wish to pay the proposed 6d per ton
wayleave. Greenwell commented: 'I did not think they would
fall in with the broad gauge but I am much mistaken if they
will not gladly ere long give sixpence a ton for the wayleave'.

With the broad gauge firmly established, it became desirable to extend the facilities it offered and a line was laid up an
incline to Tyning pit in 1857, replacing the SCC line other
than for dirt traffic.

The arrival of the main line, and its subsequent extensions
to Ludlows and Tyning, meant a considerable loss of traffic
for the SCC; and to remedy this situation, they proposed to
construct a direct tramroad branch to the GWR, enabling the
coalowners to avoid Lady Waldegrave's tolls. Unfortunately
for the coalowners, this line was never built, and the SCC had
to resign itself to a steadily decreasing traffic; by 1866, the
tramroad to Midford was 'not used by Radstock Collieries at
all, and not much by any other'.[14] The Clandown and
Writhlington companies made arrangements to avoid the
Waldegrave tolls on their coal to the GWR, and the unfortunate SCC was caught between the two interests.

In the 1870s great changes occurred. The broad-gauge line
to Radstock was converted to standard gauge and connected to
the new B & NSR line from Bristol to Radstock. The S & D

Bath extension line was opened in 1874 and the SCC tramroad to Midford was closed. Standard-gauge sidings proliferated: that to Wellsway Pit was opened on 7 January 1875 by the GWR,[15] and in 1873 the S & D signed an agreement to provide similar accommodation for Middle Pit. However, construction was delayed for eight years through fear that the GWR might derive more benefit from the line than the S & D, and the branch was not opened until 21 December 1881; it included a mixed gauge section with the remnants of the SCC tramroad, then used for carrying dirt from Middle Pit to the tips at Tyning.

After this, a gradual contraction took place. The Wellsway branch was closed in 1898, followed in 1909 by the standard-gauge branch to Tyning. The tramroad branch, converted to 2ft gauge, remained in use for dirt until 1954. Following the closure of Middle Pit in 1933 (and Clandown in 1929), the only traffic on that branch was coal for Radstock gas works. As a result of the closure of Middle Pit, the last remaining section of the SCC tramroad, used for transferring 2ft gauge tubs of dirt on 3ft 2in gauge 'dillies' from Middle Pit to the incline up to Tyning, was abandoned after 129 years of use. Middle Pit sidings were used by the Anglo-American Asphalt Co Ltd during World War II, but were closed shortly afterwards. Ludlows Pit sidings closed in 1954, along with the colliery, and in 1960 the now-redundant bridge over the S & D to Tyning was demolished.

On 7 March 1966 the S & D line through Radstock closed completely, apart from a short length serving Lower Writhlington Colliery. On the GWR side, only the former WSWR line remains in use; it is used for taking Writhlington and Kilmersdon coal on the roundabout journey to Portishead.

FROME HILL COAL DEPOT

In 1867 work began on a small coal depot at Mount Pleasant, near the top of Frome Hill.[16] It was designed to avoid the long haul up the hill out of Radstock that horses had to cope with when taking coal to Frome and surrounding districts. It was served by a single-track tramroad running up the hillside on a steep incline, worked by a stationary steam engine and boiler. The depot was completed by the end of 1868, the total cost being £977.

In due course the tramroad was converted into a double-track tramway of 2ft gauge (probably at the same time as the conversion of the line up to Tyning batches). Only coal from Ludlows pit went up to the depot; the pit tubs were run on to flat sheets at the unloading point at the top of the incline, where they were manhandled into position.

Some pitwood was brought back down the incline, which, in its double-track form, was worked by an endless rope driven from a stationary engine at its foot, the tubs being clipped on to the rope one at a time. Little else is heard of the depot except a brief mention on 10 June 1911, when it was recorded that putting out a fire there cost 1s! On 3 December 1926 the depot and incline were closed, as they had made no profit during that year. After lying derelict for some years, the yard was taken over in the 1940s by Evans foundry when the latter moved from its previous site at Lower Writhlington Colliery. Some of the original buildings still survive at the depot today and the track bed of the incline is traceable for the most part, though some portions have been absorbed into adjacent gardens.

WASHERY

In 1909 the construction of a coal-washing plant was begun in the area of land between Tyning's incline bridge and the wagon works, and by March 1910 was almost complete. Trouble with the machinery began immediately, and in June the same year it was noted that the washery was 'not yet satisfactory'. A report of 24 January 1913 stated, 'A coal washer erected several years ago by Messrs Fraser and Chalmers at Radsock . . . has been the subject of infinite trouble'. The report went on to say that the plant could only deal with 64 tons of coal per day instead of the 115 tons specified in the contract, and that it could not wash all the types of coal that had been intended. On 4 February 1922 it was still only working spasmodically.[17]

Page 189 Mackintosh Colliery: *(above)* the pithead prior to rebuilding; *(below)* the winding engine and driver, c 1895

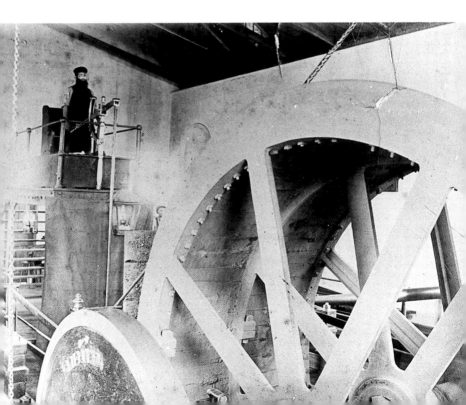

Page 190 (above) Mells Colliery c 1920. Note the horses and carts, and the bicycles stored by the heapstead; (below) Edford Colliery from the north, showing one of the traction engines used for coal haulage

The washery was served originally by both 2ft gauge and standard-gauge sidings, but between 1923 and 1931 the narrow-gauge sidings were removed. The washery closed at an unknown date and no trace remains today, the site having been obliterated in the late 1960s.

CENTRAL WORKSHOPS

Radstock Collieries' central workshops were begun in 1867 and completed in 1872 at a cost of £1,402; they replaced the old workshops at Middle Pit. Their building was the outcome of a report by Liddell on 7 March 1863, when he stated that 'the workshops for the collieries need renewing'. The new shops were located on a sharp corner of the Frome Road at Radstock, immediately opposite the Radstock Collieries' offices by Ludlows pit, and were served by a standard-gauge siding. Between 1923 and 1931 a 2ft gauge line was also built; it crossed the River Somer twice by means of steel girder bridges before entering the yard.

Railway traffic into the yard ceased with the closure of Ludlows Pit in 1954, but the NCB continued to use the stores until 1969, when the gates closed finally. Today, some of the buildings are still extant, but the site is being redeveloped.

STABLES

The Radstock Colliery stables were located in Combe End, Radstock, a short distance north of Middle Pit. Originally, each pit had its own stables, but these were later superseded by the newer ones at Combe End. At one time there were twenty-five horses kept at the stables, their duties including shunting wagons at the collieries and hauling waste material from Middle Pit to Ludlows over the tramroad. Horse haulage is believed to have ceased underground at Middle and Ludlows pits by 1930, but was retained for surface work for some years, being finally abandoned for shunting at Ludlows about 1950. The stables were finally demolished about 1966.

RADSTOCK GAS WORKS

Radstock Collieries possessed an unusual adjunct in the form

M

of Radstock Gas Works, which was situated immediately south of Middle Pit. The works were under construction on 24 September 1858, when Greenwell commented: 'the Gas Works will be very advantageous when completed'. During 1874 the works were extended at a cost of £231, five additional retorts being supplied for £138 10s 0d; a further £167 was spent on more extensions on 25 February 1877, and £171 on 27 July 1893.

Until the coming of the S & D, no rail connection was established at the works, but upon the construction of the Clandown branch line, standard-gauge sidings were provided. After the closure of Middle Pit in June 1933, coal was brought from Ludlows by rail.

The works provided all the gas used at the Radstock collieries as well as producing coal tar, etc, and survived until about 1950, by which time they had become the property of the National Coal Board. Several of the buildings survive and may be seen to this day.

Notes begin on page 259.

11 THE WRITHLINGTON COLLIERIES

Unlike the neighbouring Radstock Collieries, the pits in the Writhlington group remained under virtually the same owner-ship right up to 1947. Owned by several persons, they were not subject to decline in family fortunes as were the Waldegrave pits and they remained too powerful an entity to be absorbed into the Beauchamp empire; indeed, they were the only sub-stantial group outside it.

The first pit of importance to be sunk was Upper Writh-lington, followed by Huish and Lower Writhlington. The next two, Braysdown and Foxcote, were relative failures; the former was sold to Beauchamp in 1899, though Foxcote survived until 1931. By this date Huish and Upper Writhlington had closed and only Lower Writhlington and Kilmersdon (sunk in virgin territory in the 1870s) remained. The fact that these two pits are the last survivors in Somerset is surely a tribute to their former owners.

The central core of directors comprised W. B. Naish, W. S. Waite, Edmund Broderip, the Daubeny family and Benjamin Hansford Hill. Alban Chivers was company secretary. All these gentlemen, or their descendants, served the company for many years. The other factor contributing to stability was the colliery management; there were only three incumbents after 1865 when James Wilkins assumed the post. On his retirement he was presented with a silver cup, suitably inscribed, by the men and bailiffs of the pits. His successor, in March 1883, was J. Coulthard Walton, who was born at Alston in Cumberland in 1858 and trained at Newcastle-upon-Tyne before becoming manager at Writhlington. Following the death of the redoubtable J. Batey, the company's agent, in January 1910, Walton took on this job as well. He died on 30 May 1914 and Charles Southern became manager, remaining in this post until 1947.

All the collieries came under the ownership and management of the persons above. The owning company was variously titled; each pit used its own name as well as the amalgam— Writhlington, Foxcote & Huish Collieries, and the Writhlington Coal Co. On 6 April 1897 the latter became a limited liability company with a capital of £50,000 and bought the assets of the old company for £40,550. On 6 March 1924 the capital was increased by £20,000 to take over the nominally independent Kilmersdon Colliery Co Ltd. In 1930 the Writhlington Collieries Ltd made a loss of £2,327, but was in the black, with annual profits up to £12,626, until 1943, when a loss was made. In 1946 the loss was no less than £28,130, due primarily to the temporary closure of Kilmersdon. In 1948 the capital was halved and the company was wound up on 2 August 1956.[1]

WOODBOROUGH

Commonly called Woodborough Old Pit, there is little information about this colliery, which was perhaps the first to be sunk east of Radstock. At some period a beam pumping engine was installed, and this engine also wound coal.[2] The pit was closed by 1867 (probably in the 1840s) and became filled with water, which proved something of a hazard to Lower Writhlington Colliery, whose Middle Vein workings were once flooded out. Apart from the small dirt tips, no trace remains today.

UPPER WRITHLINGTON

This was the first of the major Writhlington pits to be sunk, work being completed in 1805, when a pumping engine was installed by J. Nash. The winding shaft was of 11ft 3in diameter and 834ft deep; it cost £6 5s per fathom to sink, and £5 per fathom for walling.[3]

In the 1860s the pit was connected to the 2ft 8½in-gauge tramway from Lower Writhlington to the GWR, which took much of the coal away. There had been an earlier proposal to

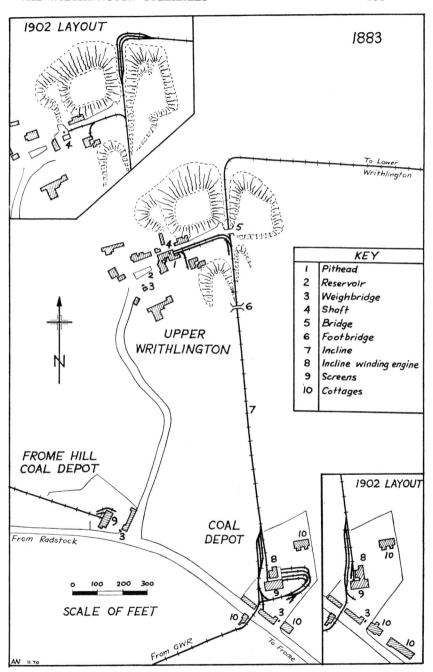

1902 LAYOUT

1883

To Lower
Writhlington

KEY

1	Pithead
2	Reservoir
3	Weighbridge
4	Shaft
5	Bridge
6	Footbridge
7	Incline
8	Incline winding engine
9	Screens
10	Cottages

UPPER
WRITHLINGTON

N

FROME HILL
COAL DEPOT

From Radstock

COAL
DEPOT

1902 LAYOUT

0   100   200   300

SCALE OF FEET

From GWR

To Frome

AN 11.70

construct a branch from the SCC tramroad to serve the colliery, but this scheme does not appear to have been carried out.[4]

The offices of the Writhlington company were at the pit for many years and part of the dirt tip was levelled out to make a tennis court for the use of officials. During 1868, the winding shaft was deepened by 108ft at the original diameter.[5] In 1883 there is a reference to the 'old pumping engine house', suggesting that the Nash engine was then disused.

In 1898 Upper Writhlington ceased coal winding; on 28 January the pit was 'practically closed', but a few men remaineed at work for some years, the site being retained as a sawmill to serve Lower Writhlington.[6] Today, the sites of some of the buildings, and the two capped shafts, are still visible. The offices and the manager's house are now private dwellings.

HUISH

On 17 July 1820 the lease of this colliery was signed by the nine proprietors, Messrs Purnell, Savage, Miles, Fussell, Broderip, Naish, Roach, Greenhill and Smith. The first coal was raised and sold in April 1824 and in 1829 the pit was rated at £720. However, the shaft must have been sunk prior to 1820 for a branch from pit bottom was begun on 30 January of that year. During August and September 1821 a 'fire engine' was erected at the colliery by J. Bond. This was lit up on 6 September and began pumping water six days later. It was soon adapted for coal winding as well, this work starting on 22 October 1823.[7]

Coal disposal was entirely by road until 1855, when a self-acting incline of 2ft 8½in gauge was laid from the pithead to sidings on the newly opened GWR line to Radstock. Four or six tubs, holding 8cwt of coal each, were let down to the GWR at a time. There was little of note about the pithead. A single two-deck cage was used in the shaft, running in 4½in square wooden guides. The upcast furnace shaft had a brick 'chimney' built round it and does not seem to have been used for either winding or pumping, being shallower than the main shaft. In 1863 it had been proposed to sink a new shaft beside the GWR but this was not carried out.

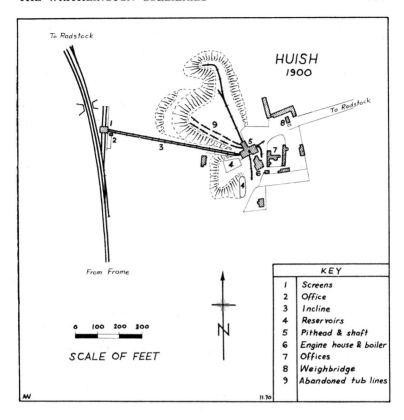

Huish was not a particularly successful colliery, employing only 70-100 men. It was closed at the end of February 1912 as uneconomic, and by May the pithead had been almost entirely demolished.[8] The most interesting relic of the pit is the 'chimney' round the upcast shaft, which still stands, as do the colliery offices. An old boiler lies in a nearby garden, and, under a rubbish heap, the original cage survives intact.

SHOSCOMBE

Shoscombe was begun about 1828 by William Coxeter James, Joseph Hill, and Mary and Frances Langford. The lease was signed on 23 May 1828 and the articles of partnership on 20 March 1829, where it was specified that the partnership should last for forty years and be known as James, Hill & Langfords.[9]

Only one shaft appears to have been sunk and this was of a peculiar section. Shaped like a bishop's mitre, it had maximum dimensions of 10ft 2in x 7ft 6in and was 360ft deep.[10] There was also a balance pit of 3ft diameter and probably of lesser depth. The site was owned by Walter Long (*see* Braysdown Colliery), hence its other name, the Long Common Coal Co. It is virtually certain that the colliery was served by a short siding off the SCC tramroad.

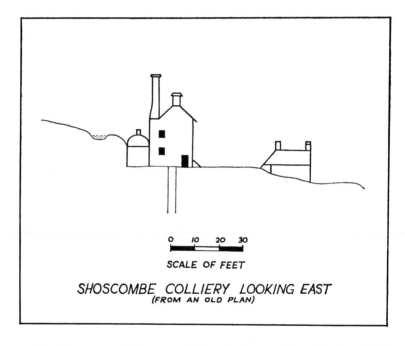

SCALE OF FEET

SHOSCOMBE COLLIERY LOOKING EAST
(FROM AN OLD PLAN)

Nothing more is known of the pit. It was closed before 1860 and today little remains other than a waterlogged depression marking the site of the shaft. The construction of the S & D main line probably obliterated many features, for the shaft was said in August 1870 to be clearly visible.

LOWER WRITHLINGTON

The two shafts of this colliery were sunk in 1829. For pumping there was a Cornish beam engine (possibly built at Paulton Foundry) working three pump lifts in the eastern shaft.

For many years, coal disposal was a sore point with the company, using as it did after 1854 the SCC tramroad to the GWR at Radstock, which cost 1s 5½d per ton, on top of the cost of 2s per ton for raising the coal 'from the bowels of the Earth in the cage'.[11] Mr Waite suggested driving a tunnel through Frome Hill to reach the GWR by a separate tramway but the estimated cost—£3,000—deterred him. But this amount was only half the sum Writhlington subscribed towards an abortive branch-line project to connect their pits direct to the GWR.[12] In the end the company built a 2ft 8½in-gauge overland tramway of its own, connecting Foxcote Colliery with Lower and Upper Writhlington, and with a loading dock on the GWR. The line was probably opened in 1867-8, including an incline up to Frome Hill, where a landsale depot was established. Horses were used on the tramway at first but the section of the line in the Somer Valley was worked by locomotives after 1882.

A standard-gauge connection from the S & D was opened in 1886, the remnants of the SCC tramroad having been used formerly to take coal back into Radstock for trans-shipment. The standard-gauge line followed the course of the SCC in many places. By 1894 the S & D main line had been doubled, the siding becoming the down main line, and a direct junction to the colliery was put in, together with storage sidings to the east.

The coal winding shaft was deepened to 1,461ft soon after to work the Farrington Series coal. The pumping shaft was not deepened and about 1939 electric pumps replaced the Cornish engine, which fell into disuse and was broken up for scrap during World War II. It had a cylinder approximately 48in x 72in.

Throughout the pit's life, dirt has been tipped to the west of the pithead, south of the S & D. At first, narrow-gauge lines ran out to the tips, tubs being worked by a haulage engine at the pithead; but after about 1940 road dumpers were used for this work.

Lower Writhlington remained largely unchanged until nationalisation. In 1953 a 700yd road was driven into the Braysdown Colliery workings, and during 1959 a second con-

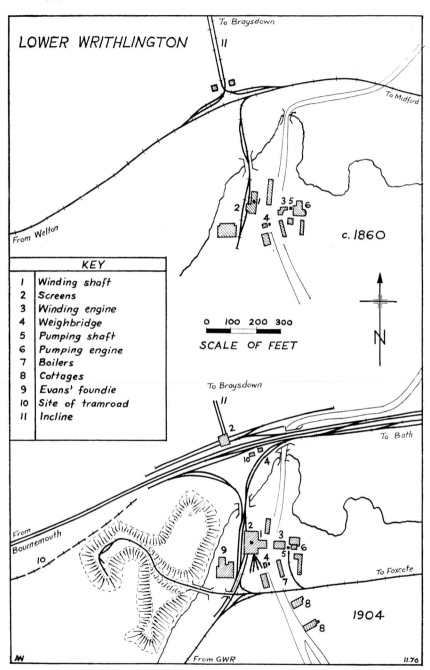

LOWER WRITHLINGTON

c. 1860

To Braysdown

To Midford

From Welton

KEY

1	Winding shaft
2	Screens
3	Winding engine
4	Weighbridge
5	Pumping shaft
6	Pumping engine
7	Boilers
8	Cottages
9	Evans' foundie
10	Site of tramroad
11	Incline

0   100 200 300

SCALE OF FEET

N

To Braysdown

To Bath

From Bournemouth

To Foxcote

1904

From GWR

11.70

nection, 1,315yd long, was made to Kilmersdon Colliery. Surface improvements were also carried out. In May 1954 new screens were approved at an estimated cost of £55,000, while steel tubs replaced the old 9½cwt capacity wooden ones.[13] No pithead baths were built, men being conveyed to and from the baths at Ludlows Colliery in buses. In 1966 the steam winding engine, the last to be used for regular coal work in Somerset, was replaced by the electric engine from Norton Hill Colliery. The steam winder, built about 1870 by J. D. Leigh of Manchester, had 28in x 60in cylinders and a drum of 12ft 3in diameter. It wound two double-deck cages carrying one tub per deck, and was supplied with steam from a rank of Lancashire boilers, the oldest of which had been built by Adamson in 1909 and worked at 50psi.

The plate on page 137 shows Writhlington viewed from the hillside below Braysdown Colliery and this is still the best view of the pit today. There have been numerous changes since this photograph was taken, but one can still gain the impression—and a reminder—of Somerset mining as it must have been in its heyday.

BRAYSDOWN

The principal partners in the Braysdown Colliery Co were George Daubeny and John Scobell, and work on the colliery appears to have begun about 1840; coal winding had certainly started in 1845.[14] To carry the coal, an incline down to the SCC tramroad was built following an agreement dated 23 March 1855 between the SCC and Walter Long. This line remained in use until after 1874, when it was replaced by a 2ft 6in-gauge edge railway incline to exchange sidings and screens on the S & D.

In or about 1862 the winding shaft was sunk to the Farrington Series, the deepening being circular—10ft diameter—and reaching a depth of 1,740ft, the deepest shaft in Somerset at the time. In July 1911 the shaft was further sunk to 1,834ft, while a crossmeasure drift driven in about 1933 proved the No 9 seam at 2,448ft.

The 1862 deepening was disastrous. McMurtrie said that it

had 'turned out very badly indeed'[15] while the colliery manager admitted that the Farrington seams were 'valueless'.[16]
The pit also laboured under the high cost (2s 5½d per ton) of
taking coal to the GWR. But it did have one point in its favour—an excellent safety record. Between 1848 and 1864 there
were only five fatal accidents.

In 1899 the colliery was sold to Frank B. Beauchamp, who,
due to lease troubles, was unable to work the pit for some
years.[17] It passed into the ownership of his Somerset Collieries
Ltd and, after about 1920, was managed jointly with Camerton Colliery, sharing many specialist staff. A connection between the two pits was made and Braysdown pumping shaft
became the upcast for Camerton. A further connection, between Braysdown and Ludlows Colliery in the Farrington
Series, meant that the latter became the Braysdown upcast
shaft. This connection was made on 9 May 1934, the existing
road to Camerton being duplicated about this time.

Over the years 1937-46, Braysdown produced about 50,000
tons of coal per year, at an average profit of £7,023; this output was well below the potential maximum output of 75,000
tons. Coal-cutting machines were introduced in 1942, but removed by 1946 as unsatisfactory.[18]

In 1946 the main winding engine was a 26in x 48in two-
cylinder type built by J. D. Leigh of Manchester; a similar
engine, with 20in x 36in cylinders, was used on the second
shaft. Underground, all mining was in the Nos 5, 6 and 9
seams, the Radstock Series workings having been shut down.
Between 230 and 250 men were employed at the colliery,
which was valued at £69,724.

Under the NCB, few changes were made. Output remained
at pre-war levels and, though productivity increased, the pit
had costs in materials far exceeding those of any other Somerset pit. The workings were very extensive, over twenty-five
haulage engines being used underground, and even in 1929
the pit had been considered uneconomic. The closing years of
Braysdown have a complex history. Following the closure of
Camerton in 1950, Braysdown depended on Ludlows for its
emergency egress and much of its pumping. This work saved

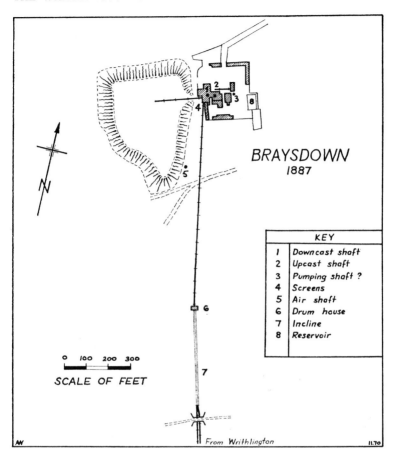

BRAYSDOWN
1887

	KEY
1	Downcast shaft
2	Upcast shaft
3	Pumping shaft ?
4	Screens
5	Air shaft
6	Drum house
7	Incline
8	Reservoir

0   100   200   300

SCALE OF FEET

From Writhlington

Braysdown £9,000 to £10,000 a year, and when on 29 September 1953 it was proposed to close Ludlows, plans were laid to enable Braysdown to cope with the 1,250,000 gallons of water that Ludlows pumped each week. New pumps were required, as well as a new fan, before Braysdown could operate independently. In the same year, it was stated that the pit had an 'unlimited' life expectancy.[19]

The works now undertaken show a curious contradiction in purpose. On the one hand, plans were made for the construction of new pithead baths and for replacing the incline to the main line by a conveyor belt; against this, a road was driven in 1953 from Lower Writhlington into the Braysdown No 5 seam workings, with the intention of winding Braysdown coal at Writhlington.

On Monday 13 August 1956, at 2pm, the new pithead baths were opened with all due ceremony,[20] having cost £28,000; but almost immediately coal winding at Braysdown ceased. Little or no coal was brought up the Writhlington shaft from the Braysdown workings, and the new connection was virtually unused. A few men continued to use the new baths until April 1958. The colliery was permanently closed on 29 October 1959, after dams had been put in to protect the Writhlington workings. Surface machinery either salvaged or sold for scrap included the winding engines, and equipment from the baths was sent to New Rock Colliery in 1961.[21]

The site remained almost intact until January 1970, when it was completely demolished. Only the pithead baths, used by a pet-food firm, still stand.

FOXCOTE

The earliest mention of this pit is in a lease of 25 March 1853 by which the Foxcote Colliery Co leased minerals from Sir John Smyth of the Foxcote estates. This appears to be the sinking lease and the shaft, 1,212ft deep, was opened about January 1859.[22] Because of water problems, however, it was used only down to 954ft.

Foxcote was not a very successful pit. In 1864 it was said that the sinking had been 'attended with an unusual amount of difficulty and danger', and in 1871 the outlook was described as 'uncertain'.[23] The proprietors did not agree with these views, deepening the shaft to 1,416ft in 1870-1,[24] and hoping that the first seam of the Farrington Series, cut by April 1871, would produce an amount of coal 'altogether surprising' in the district. Output was about 600 tons per week in 1930, probably as high a figure as at any period.

For coal disposal, 2ft 8½in-gauge tramways were used to carry coal down to Lower Writhlington Colliery, or to take it out to a coal depot at Turner's Tower. The latter tramway was worked by *Foxcote*, a Hudswell Clarke 0 – 6 – 0 saddle tank

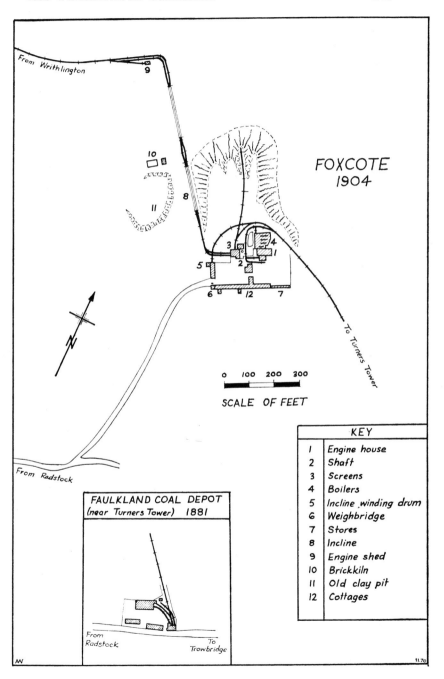

FOXCOTE
1904

SCALE OF FEET

0   100   200   300

From Writhlington

From Radstock

To Turners Tower

N

FAULKLAND COAL DEPOT
(near Turners Tower) 1881

From Radstock

To Trowbridge

KEY	
1	Engine house
2	Shaft
3	Screens
4	Boilers
5	Incline winding drum
6	Weighbridge
7	Stores
8	Incline
9	Engine shed
10	Brickkiln
11	Old clay pit
12	Cottages

locomotive built in 1890. The incline down to Writhlington was apparently built by 1866.[25]

Apart from the usual pithead equipment, the colliery also possessed a small brickworks, closed by 1924, which supplied bricks for use in shaft repairs. The winding engine at the pit was built by Paulton Foundry and wound two double-deck cages.

Coal winding ceased in February 1931.[26] The pithead was demolished in the 1950s, and, apart from the foundations of the winding engine, the drum house at the head of the incline, and the trackbeds of the tramways, there is little to see.

KILMERSDON

In November 1872 Lord Hylton of Ammerdown decided to grant the Writhlington proprietors a lease of all his Upper Series coal under the Ammerdown estates, an area of about 328 acres. If Writhlington declined the lease, it was to be offered to Countess Waldegrave at £600pa for the use of the Radstock Collieries.[27]

Such were the beginnings of Kilmersdon Colliery; the Writhlington proprietors had no intention of refusing such a valuable property and they formed the Kilmersdon Colliery Co to sink and work the pit. The lease was signed on 25 December 1873 and sinking began on 6 February 1874. A winding engine was supplied for the pumping shaft by Paulton Foundry in 1875.

Progress was slow due to geological difficulties and by June 1877 the shaft had only reached 540ft. Work on the winding shaft (10ft 6in diameter) began in October 1876 and, towards the end of 1877, the shafts had reached their completed depth of 858ft. The first coal was sold by April 1878. To carry the coal a standard-gauge railway and self-acting incline was laid to the GWR Frome – Radstock line, the agreement being signed on 1 September 1877. In 1889 the layout of the railway was altered to the arrangement that exists today. Initially horses were used to work the traffic, the first known locomotive arriving in 1896. The present Peckett locomotive was sent to the colliery on 10 September 1929 and has worked here ever

Page 207 Newbury Colliery: (above) the pithead viewed from the west, showing the tubline to Mackintosh; (below) an underground view, reproduced from a broken glassplate negative. The lad at bottom left is wearing the guss and crook, the only known photograph of the device in use

Page 208 (above) New Rock Colliery in 1968, showing (left to right) boiler chimney, escape shaft and winding shaft; *(below)* Mendip Colliery in 1968, soon after closure

since. Diesel locomotives have been introduced but have not proved satisfactory.

About 1900 (certainly before December 1904) the shafts were deepened to cut the Farrington seams, the total depth being 1,582ft. The Evans winding engine, a duplicate of the 1875 engine mentioned above, had two 26in x 60in cylinders and was unsuitable for winding from this new depth; so a new engine, built by Worsley Mesnes, with 28in x 60in cylinders was substituted.[28] The Cornish beam engine that pumped the Radstock Series workings remained in use until about 1929, when it was scrapped and replaced by underground pumps and tank-winding.

On 6 April 1897 the company was formed into a limited liability undertaking, and on 6 March 1924 the agreement whereby Writhlington purchased Kilmersdon was signed.[29] In 1928, in response to agitation by the miners over the use of the guss, the colliery's first conveyor face was started.[30] Pithead baths were installed in 1934 and extended in 1940. By 1939 there were four conveyor faces in operation, and the pit's output overaged 70,000 tons a year.[31] By 1940 an emergency connection to Lower Writhlington was completed, this connection being duplicated by the NCB in 1959. Kilmersdon shaft became upcast and Lower Writhlington shaft downcast.

In May 1946 the lower part of the upcast and pumping shaft fell in, which caused some flooding and shut the colliery down for six months. A week after the mishap all the ponies were brought out of the pit, the shaft then being partly filled with ashes that were then stabilised by cementation. This work lasted into 1947, the NCB thus inheriting a temporary 'dead duck'. In due course the pit was reopened but had not been back in operation for more than two years when old workings were holed and it was flooded. Tank winding was resorted to for removing the accumulated water and tanks were still in use in 1955, removing 30,000 gallons of water each day.[32]

Up to 29 October 1958, £82,000 had been invested at Kilmersdon by the NCB, but, in the preceeding twelve months alone, there had been a profit of £83,000. Investment was very low compared to, say, Norton Hill, and should be seen in the

N

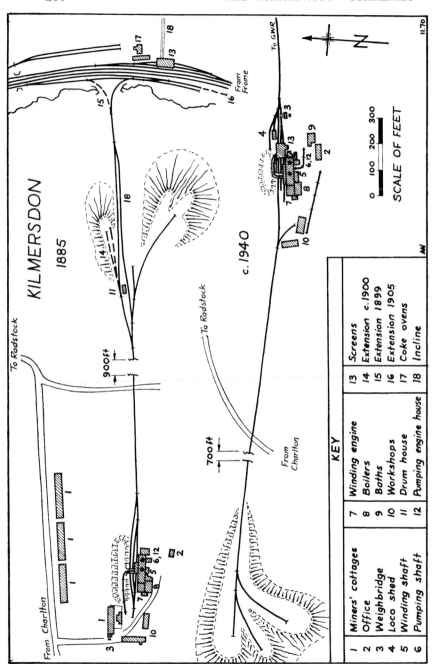

KILMERSDON

1885

c.1940

To Radstock

From Charlton

From Frome

To GWR

From Charlton

To Radstock

900ft

700ft

N

11.70

SCALE OF FEET

0   100   200   300

KEY

1	Miners' cottages	7	Winding engine	13	Screens
2	Office	8	Boilers	14	Extension c.1900
3	Weighbridge	9	Baths	15	Extension 1899
4	Loco shed	10	Workshops	16	Extension 1905
5	Winding shaft	11	Drum house	17	Coke ovens
6	Pumping shaft	12	Pumping engine house	18	Incline

context of a total investment of £1,600,000 in the Bristol & Somerset coalfield, which had resulted in a loss of £6,500,000 since 1947.[33]

Steam winding survived at Kilmersdon until 12 August 1963, when a 650hp electric winder from Airth Colliery in Scotland was commissioned on the coaling shaft, together with three-deck cages and steel tubs with a capacity of 19cwt of coal. In 1965 the steam winder on the pumping shaft was also replaced by an electric engine, mainly because the Lancashire boilers were in poor shape. Early in 1966 the redundant colliery chimney was felled—in a very confined space—by Dawsons of Clutton. That year was also the first since 1957 in which a loss had been made; in the financial year 1964-5 there had been a profit of £131,000.[34]

After the closure of Norton Hill in 1966, the three battery locomotives were transferred to Kilmersdon and two have been put into service underground. Together with coal-cutting machines and trunk conveyor belts, such improvements have enabled Kilmersdon to survive in the modern era. Two of the colliery's standard-gauge locomotives have been bought for preservation, but the Peckett 0-4-0 saddle tank still provides a touch of nostalgia.

Notes begin on page 269.

12 BEAUCHAMP'S GOLD MINE

SOMERSET COLLIERIES LTD AND THE BEAUCHAMP FAMILY

The Beauchamp family was the most powerful single group of Somerset colliery owners. Most of the county's pits came into the hands of one or more members of the family, at least in the pits' later lives. It is no denigration of the family's capability to say that the two surviving collieries in Somerset were never in the Beauchamp group; rather, during the era of private ownership each pit was worked to its limit and thus had only a short life expectancy after nationalisation.

Arguably the first venture into coalmining was that of William Beachim at Vobster Colliery, where he was manager in 1866.[1] Two years later he started the Radstock Coal Co and the Radstock Wagon Co, in partnership with Theophilus Gullick. The title of the former business so aggravated the Waldegrave coal interests that in 1878 a legal action was commenced to prevent Beachim using a company name that suggested he was the owner of a colliery in Radstock when he did not. Two years earlier, in 1876, Beachim adopted his family title and publicly changed his name to William Beachim Beauchamp.[2] His coal-factoring business was on a semi-national scale and he eventually became the owner of three collieries in Somerset—Farrington, Old Welton and Welton Hill. In addition, by 1883 he owned the Hallatrow Pennant Stone Quarries at Cloud Hill, Hallatrow.

William Beauchamp died on 1 March 1894 after a long illness, leaving three sons. Frank was born in 1866 and received his father's coal properties. In partnership with his younger brother, Louis, he reopened Norton Hill Colliery in 1896 and sank the new shaft there in 1900. Frank and Louis also worked Farrington Colliery in equal partnership, together with the Radstock Coal & Wagon Co (an amalgamation of their father's two companies). The Norton Hill company had a capital of £21,337, and the Farrington and Radstock companies were capitalised at £28,646.[3]

Frank acquired collieries on his own account—Braysdown about 1899 and Camerton in 1914—and in 1925 bought the Radstock Collieries, his father's old adversary.[4] The pits at Dunkerton and Priston were also bought in the 1920s.

Colonel Sir Frank Beauchamp, Bart, CBE, JP, was created the first baronet in 1918 and, with an increasing number of acquisitions, formed Somerset Collieries Ltd to take over his leases and property. The company was registered on 26 September 1925 with a capital of £50,000.[5] By the contract, signed on 23 December 1925, Sir Frank granted to the new company the leases of Ludlows, Middle Pit, Wellsway, Tyning and Dunkerton; the mining leases of Braysdown, Clandon, Camerton, Priston and Conygre; his freehold coal at Timsbury; and all other colliery properties in Somerset. Sir Frank was company chairman with his sons Douglas Clifford (born 1903) and Ian (born 1907) as directors.

It will be noticed that Norton Hill, colloquially known as 'Beauchamp's Gold Mine' and the most important colliery in Somerset, was not included in the sale. SCL held an extraordinary general meeting on 14 November 1935 at which it was resolved to change the name of the company to Radstock Collieries Ltd, this change supposedly occurring on 5 December 1935.[6] In fact, the name of the company formed on this date was the same as that of the first, ie Somerset Collieries Ltd, with the difference that the new company was a public one, with a capital of £375,000. It was formed from Norton Hill Collieries Ltd, Radstock Coal Co, Radstock Wagon Co, Radstock Gas Works, Radstock Collieries Ltd, and the interests in Somerset of Sir Frank and Louis that had not been incorporated in 1925, such as coal leases at Clandown and Old Welton. The second SCL was promoted under the Mining Industry Act of 1926 and it had four working pits—Norton Hill, Camerton, Braysdown and Ludlows—employing 1,400 men.

Sir Frank seems to have split up his interests; the name Radstock Collieries Ltd remained in being, taking over the coal marketing side of the business. On the same date as the second SCL was formed, it signed a dividend pooling agreement with RCL. Sir Frank owned all the 168,978 £1 ordinary shares in SCL and 46,998 shares in RCL, which in addition held 109,471 shares in SCL.[7] It should be emphasised that Somerset Collieries Ltd was the title used by the pits.

One significant advantage accrued from the formation of the new company. Before December 1935 only 3 per cent of mining royalties were in the hands of colliery companies but, with the formation of the second SCL, and Sir Frank's earlier buying-up of leases, this figure was increased to 23 per cent.[8]

The output figures for SCL reveal the considerable size of its operations:[9]

Year	Tons Raised	Year	Tons Raised
1930	187,910	1938	307,389
1931	190,427	1939	301,049
1932	169,762	1940	306,826
1933(i)	160,145	1941	288,612
1934	160,712	1942	294,762
1935	196,658	1943	295,505
1936(ii)	303,773	1944	286,025
1937	316,879	1945	258,694
		1946	262,827

(i) Middle Pit closed
(ii) First year including Norton Hill output

These figures represent 43 per cent of the commercially disposable coal produced in Somerset during this period. In 1946 SCL was valued at £538,653 for the purpose of compensation under nationalisation, but the actual amount received was only £250,244. Profits made by the first SCL averaged £40,000 per annum, while the gross trading profits of the second company during its first five years averaged £64,000, helped by the results from Norton Hill and the closing of less favoured pits.[10]

On 31 December 1946, at the end of the private era, Sir Frank's service with SCL was terminated and he received a £3,000 'golden handshake'. At the time he was lying ill at Eastbourne, whence he wrote to ask for a larger payment. His fellow directors were unable to agree to this, pointing out that he had only been entitled to £750.[11] There is little doubt that Sir Frank felt poorly treated and he died on 17 June 1950. He had worked in Somerset mining for over 50 years and even today no name is mentioned more frequently in the coalfield than his.

Louis Beauchamp died in 1947 but Ian and Douglas continued with SCL, which was finally wound up on 26 June 1959. Douglas was created second baronet and continued with the National Coal Board for some years under his commonly used title of Sir Peter Beauchamp.

We can conclude by briefly mentioning some of the other family ramifications in the mining world. Both Sir Frank and Ian were directors of East Bristol Collieries Ltd up to 1948, though that company had ceased mining a decade earlier. New Rock Colliery was bought by Louis and his son Guy, and Louis also owned Moorewood in its declining years. The final mining venture was by another branch of the family. William Beauchamp's third son, Walter, had four sons—Ralph, Dudley, Ross and Gilbert—who went into partnership in the Mells Quarry Co and, later, at Charmborough Colliery.[12] This was the last new mine to be opened in Somerset but was an almost complete failure.

Gradually the Beauchamp pits were shut, the last and greatest, Norton Hill, closing in 1966. Over the countryside the family houses—Newbury House, Stratton House, Norton Hall—still stand. Only Sir Frank's Woodborough House, demolished after the NCB vacated it in favour of other offices, has gone. But even without such physical remains the memory of the Beauchamps will survive in Somerset as long as the memory of coalmining itself.

THE NORTON HILL COLLIERIES

The earliest mention of Norton Hill Colliery is 1839, when

a 'New Coal Works' owned by the Norton Hill Coal Co is
referred to on land owned by Major Thomas Savage.[13] It is
possible that Messrs Spink and Beaumont were concerned
with this company; however, the pit does not appear to have
been sunk at this time. The first known lease from Savage,
granted on 1 May 1846 to W. L. Parsons, three members of
the Rees-Mogg family and three other partners, gave permission to sink the shaft.[14] The colliery was situated close to the
Radstock–Shepton Mallet road.

Little coal was proved to the north of the pit because of
the presence of the Radstock Slide Fault, and on 24 May 1867
the lessees gave notice of their intention to close the pit and
terminate the lease within three months, 'by reason of the
mine having proved unproductive'.[15]

The colliery was laid out on conventional lines with two
shafts of 4ft 6in diameter and 1,247ft deep. The winding engine was of the beam type, rare in Somerset but common in
the metalliferous mines of Cornwall, as was the pumping engine. A new 36in cylinder arrived at the pit in April 1861 for
one of these engines.

In or before 1896 the colliery was bought by Frank and
Louis Beauchamp. Plans for a siding off the S&D were
approved in April 1898, in which year the lease of the pit was
signed, and the siding was made under an agreement dated
18 April 1900. This branch line doubtless carried materials
for the reopening, since little of the remaining machinery was
usable. The first job was the installation of a compound horizontal pumping engine, which worked what was apparently
the original pump fixed in the shaft. However, the initial
draining of the shaft was by a 40 gallon drum and hand wind-
lass. As soon as coal was reached, men were set to work in
order to offset the costs of the pumping. For winding, a two-
cylinder horizontal engine was erected, with cylinders 22in x
48in and a parallel drum 10ft in diameter.

It was not intended that the colliery should resume commercial production; instead, an entirely new shaft was to be
sunk about 500yd to the north, after which the old shafts
would only be used for ventilation and emergency. This plan

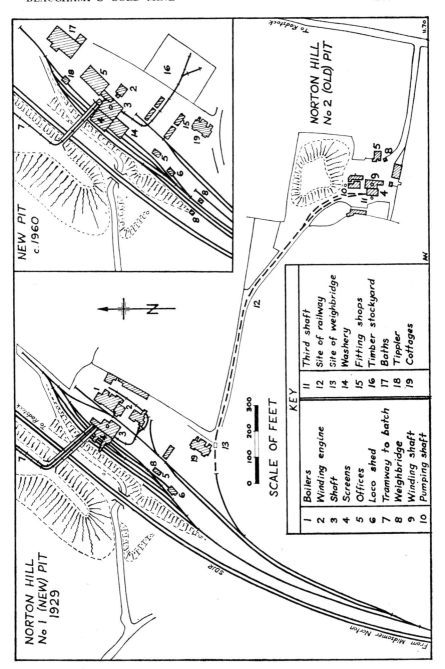

NEW PIT c.1960

NORTON HILL No 2 (OLD) PIT

NORTON HILL No 1 (NEW) PIT 1929

To Radstock

To Radstock

From Midsomer Norton

SCALE OF FEET

0   100   200   300

KEY

1 Boilers
2 Winding engine
3 Shaft
4 Screens
5 Offices
6 Loco shed
7 Tramway to batch
8 Weighbridge
9 Winding shaft
10 Pumping shaft
11 Third shaft
12 Site of railway
13 Site of weighbridge
14 Washery
15 Fitting shops
16 Timber stockyard
17 Baths
18 Tippler
19 Cottages

had the advantage of economy and the money was expended to give what was, at the time of opening, the largest colliery Somerset had ever seen.

Sinking of the new shaft began about 1900 and was finished in 1903.[16] With a diameter of 13ft 6in and a depth of 1,503ft, it was brick-lined throughout and overcame the difficulties of mining at the old pit, sinking through the Radstock Slide Fault. Mining at Old Pit appears to have ceased by December 1903, after the completion of a branch between the two pits.

Under an agreement of 20 July 1903 a new siding was built to serve the screens at the new pit. Spanning the tracks was a gantry carrying two lines of 2ft 5½in gauge tub rails, enabling dirt to be tipped between the colliery and the S & D. Further siding accommodation was provided by agreements of 10 February 1905 and 23 March 1907.

Only a few years after the opening of the pit, there was a major disaster. At 10pm on the night of Thursday, 9 April 1908, ten men were killed by a coal-dust explosion underground.[17] At 11.30pm that night, Mr Attwood (under-manager at Norton Hill) and two employees, T. Chivers and W. Goold, descended the shaft to rescue anyone who might have survived. Nothing was heard from this party and so a second was sent underground. By 5am on Friday there had been no word from either party and so Mr Edgell (under-manager at Farrington) formed a third rescue party to investigate.

Underground, both rescue parties were found alive but dazed, having become lost in the smoke-filled workings. The only exception was Chivers of the first party who had been overcome by fumes and left for dead. Edgell, by breathing through a damp handkerchief, managed to find Chivers and bring him to the surface where, miraculously, he survived. He had been unconscious underground almost ten hours.

At the enquiry into the explosion it was revealed that the ten men who died had been firing gelignite shots without taking any precautions to damp down the dust. Despite identical explosions at Camerton and Timsbury, it was concluded that few, if any, managers of Somerset collieries considered coal dust to be an explosive agent.

There was another, less serious, accident on 10 November 1908 when a man was injured by a moving railway wagon that was being pulled to the screens by a traction engine. By 1909, however, a locomotive was at work in the sidings. In this year a tub bridge was built across the S & D to reach a new dirt tipping area to the north.

A report of 1913 gives some details of the layout at New Pit. Because coal was wound from two landings, the winding engine had a split drum, the smaller diameter carrying the rope for the upper landing. The headgear was wooden, 45ft high, and was replaced in the 1930s by a steel headgear from the closed Dunkerton Colliery.

Under a lease of 24 June 1925 mining was extended into the Welton area and, about December 1939, a connection was made to the deep shaft at Old Welton Colliery, this shaft being reopened for ventilation and emergency use.

Throughout the 1930s Norton Hill was the largest producer in Somerset, with an annual output of over 125,000 tons. In 1939 there was an output of 130,817 tons, and in 1947, in contrast to most pits after the war, 149,000 tons were raised. The average annual profit in the ten years to 1946 was £50,000 and the value of £121,506 placed on the colliery shows it to have been by far the biggest and most important in Somerset.

The 1946-7 survey of the pit said that its plant and buildings were generally adequate, but 'some attention should be paid to reducing manual labour between pit and wagon'. Old Pit, fitted with a two-deck cage for men only, was an upcast shaft originally but, when the connection to Old Welton was made, Old Pit and Old Welton became downcasts and New Pit upcast. At the latter the original winding engine was still in service, with two 24in x 60in cylinders, and supplied with steam from four 100psi Lancashire boilers. The engine was capable of raising 600 tons of coal per $7\frac{1}{2}$ hour shift. To work tubs out to the tip there was an endless rope system across the bridge, powered by a 10hp motor.

Underground, things were less satisfactory. There were no less than 21,095 yards of 14lb tub track, including 110 points and no conveyor belts. During 1938 a coal-cutter had been tried but was removed as unsuitable. For handling coal tubs there were neither creepers nor tipplers; in short, though the pit was modern in many ways, mining was still in the traditional Somerset style.

The position was that the colliery appeared to have a good life ahead of it, subject to modernisation, with over 6 million tons of coal reserves. A reorganisation plan was produced by NCB in August 1948 under which an estimated £543,499 would be spent over about four years. The planned output afterwards would be a maximum of 315,000 tons per annum, or 250,000 tons in normal working, far in excess of anything seen in Somerset before. To achieve this, the existing labour force of 750 men would be increased to 900; after rebuilding, a work force of 830 men was visualised.[18]

Norton Hill was moreover the only pit in Somerset then making a profit, of 5s 1d per ton. The existing output was 3,000 tons per week in 1947, 1,000 tons of which was sold to the landsale trade.

So many items were proposed for renewal under the plan that, apart from the shaft, little remained of the original colliery. The plans were approved in December 1948, when £500,000 was allocated for the work which began in March 1949. The first building to be completed was the new pithead baths and medical centre, opened in January 1951 at a cost of £57,130. Up to the end of 1952, £366,616 had been spent, mostly on surface alterations.

New screens were in use by April 1951, together with a new tub circuit on the surface. The old screens were then demolished to make way for a new Baum washer, brought into use in August 1952. In 1953, a new 640hp electric winding engine was installed, starting work on 10 August, after which the steam winder and boilers were scrapped. The first of 500 new 26cu ft steel mine cars was also brought into use, together with a new tippler on the batch. By July, the new standard-gauge sidings had been completed. Originally, empty wagons arrived on the screen roads and were worked on a rising gradient by a stationary haulage engine which pulled them from the screens to the end of the sidings. Here they were picked up by one of the colliery locomotives and taken to the 'full' sidings via a line running between the winding engine and the pithead. Under the new arrangements, the latter line was done away with, the colliery locomotive hauling the empties up past the screens, to which the wagons could then run down by gravity for loading and remarshalling. A second weighbridge was installed for this new pattern of work.

Underground railways also came in for attention with the introduction in 1951 of three 10 ton battery locomotives built by Greenwood & Batley. Two of these locomotives were in regular use by 1952, the first locomotives in a Somerset coalmine. They survived until 1960 when the districts they were serving were abandoned and, in October 1962, the first locomotive was returned to its makers for regauging to 2ft 8½in, for service at Kilmersdon Colliery.

In 1960 further modernisation was begun. Electric winding engines were put in at Old Pit and Old Welton shafts, and the replacement of the wooden tubs by mine cars was completed. Cages carrying only one tub per deck were introduced to speed up changeover times at the top and bottom of the shaft. The underground workings were concentrated into No 7 seam, in which three mechanised faces were brought into use. All the coal then came to the bottom landing, split level winding having ceased since the introduction of the new winder.

Such modernisation resulted in what was, to all intents and purposes, a new colliery, but Norton Hill was still unable to work at a profit, one reason being the low selling price—64s 11d per ton of coal—which could only be profitable with a larger output. Output could not be increased because of the limitations of the main haulage incline, 840yd against a gradient of 1 in 4. To overcome this, an expenditure of £23,000 was allocated late in 1962 for the installation of a 36in wide conveyor belt on the incline. The work was carried out in 1963 and the belt came into use after the Easter holiday.,

The result was immediate. All the coal produced by the plough faces could now be got away without stopping the faces for the incline to 'catch up' with output. In May 1963 came the welcome news that a profit of 3s 6d per ton was being made, a great contrast to the average loss of 15s 8d per ton during 1962. The first steps in modernisation had improved OMS from 19.9cwt in 1947 to 28.9cwt in 1962; and the new belt gave a further improvement to 36.5cwt in 1963. The national average OMS for 1963 was 33.6cwt, clearly showing the improvements made at Norton Hill.

On the railway sidings innovations were also made. Since 1953 the sole locomotive at work had been *Lord Salisbury*, a venerable 16in x 22in 0-6-0 saddle tank. To replace it, a specification was drawn up in 1964 for a six-coupled diesel hydraulic locomotive with a 340-80hp engine, to be capable of working traffic up the maximum siding gradient of 1 in 35. But no money was forthcoming for this replacement, and, instead, an 0-4-0 side tank locomotive built by Hunslet in 1931 arrived from the Phoenix Fuel Works in Port Talbot during September 1964. It proved satisfactory and on 24 March 1965, it was decided to sell *Lord Salisbury* for scrap.[19]

It is perhaps surprising that, despite modernisation, Norton Hill soon lapsed into unprofitability. In 1965 the pit went on to single shift working in an effort to curb the mounting losses. Geological difficulties, together with an increasing manpower shortage, were primarily responsible for the losses. The decision was taken to close the pit and the last coal was wound at 8.45pm on 11 February 1966. Only 284 men were then employed at the pit, and about 100 were retained for salvage work; this ceased in May and the site was handed over to contractors on 9 May. Surface machinery was removed during the ensuing months and, by October, the shaft had been filled in with rubble and dirt, the headgear and screens had gone and the locomotive had been transferred to Kilmersdon Colliery. Old Pit and Old Welton remained almost intact into 1967 but were then demolished and their shafts sealed. The New Pit winding engine was transferred to Lower Writhlington Colliery for further service, the decision being taken in March 1966 for implementation in July.

If we may end on a personal note, one of us was taken on an underground tour at Norton Hill during the salvage operations and the scale and apparent permanence of the workings were deeply impressive. Looking at the flattened area today it seems hard to believe that the largest colliery in Somerset has actually gone forever. There is a small mound of dirt marking the position of the 'best shaft in Somerset'; apart from the derelict pithead baths, the locomotive shed and weigh-houses, that is all that remains.

Notes begin on page 270.

13 THE NETTLEBRIDGE VALLEY

THE SMALLER MENDIP COLLIERIES

From Gurney Slade eastward to Mells there have been many hundreds of small workings. Few lasted beyond 1800 but their ancestry can be traced back at least six centuries. To serve as an introduction to the main pits in the area, this section will be devoted to a description of some of these early pits.

Probably the most southerly coal seam outcrops in the west of this region are the Red and White Axen (or Aken) veins, whose course can be predicted eastwards until they are cut out by a fault at Nettlebridge. These seams and those above them —in order, the Perrink, Main Coal, Stone Rag, Fern Rag and Standing veins—have been worked since the earliest times. At the south-western 'corner' of the coalfield, these seams are covered by Triassic clays and conglomerates, but many pits were still sunk through to the coal. The northern outcrops lie in Chilcompton parish and it is likely that most of the pits ascribed to this parish lay in the region of Blacker's Hill.[1]

South-east from the Old Down Inn were the Stock Hill pits at Blacker's Hill. In 1693, a waterwheel was used to drain Catcutt's Pit in the same area, but the latest to operate appears to have been Chilcompton New Pit, at work in 1824. About the same time a pit was a work at Emborough, though in 1791 this had been said to be 'discontinued'. To the south were other small pits at Ashwick[2] and, northwards, the Ston Easton collieries, six being at work in 1794. Immediately east of Nettlebridge is Stratton Common and this, being probably the site of the earliest collieries in Somerset, will be considered in more detail.

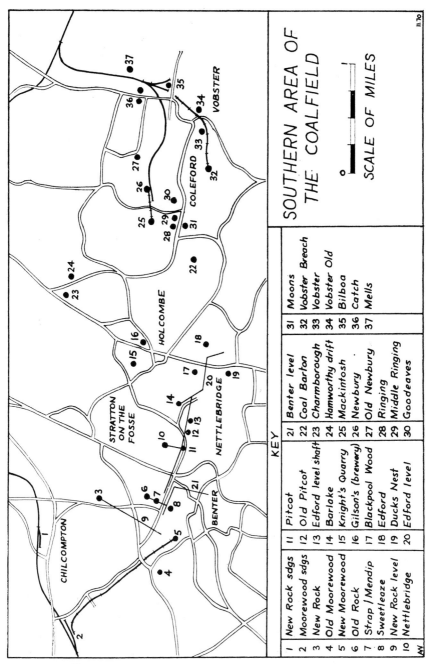

SOUTHERN AREA OF
THE COALFIELD

SCALE OF MILES

KEY

1	New Rock sdgs	11	Pitcot	21	Benter level	31	Moons
2	Moorewood sdgs	12	Old Pitcot	22	Coal Barton	32	Vobster Breach
3	New Rock	13	Edford level shaft	23	Charmborough	33	Vobster
4	Old Moorewood	14	Barlake	24	Hamworthy drift	34	Vobster Old
5	New Moorewood	15	Knight's Quarry	25	Mackintosh	35	Bilboa
6	Old Rock	16	Gilson's (brewery)	26	Newbury	36	Catch
7	Strap / Mendip	17	Blackpool Wood	27	Old Newbury	37	Mells
8	Sweetleaze	18	Edford	28	Ringing		
9	New Rock level	19	Ducks Nest	29	Middle Ringing		
10	Nettlebridge	20	Edford level	30	Goodeaves		

P

The area concerned is a little over half a mile square. It is largely bare of covering rock deposits except at the northern limits, where the coal measures are overlain by dolomitic conglomerates, and the whole area is peppered with the tumps of early workings. Even today it is possible to trace the coal outcrops—black lines against the brown earth of ploughed fields.

It was mentioned in the Introduction that if the Romans dug coal, then they probably did so on Stratton Common. Other than this, the earliest references are to the pits on the Manor lands at Stratton, which were being worked as early as 1300. Various bell pits were in use throughout the succeeding centuries, though possibly working was intermittent. In 1443 the Manor pits sold coal worth £2 1s 1d. When the demesne lands were leased by John Horner in 1544, coal was only of secondary importance, and by 1586 it was said to be used only by smiths for ironworking.[3]

There were other pits here. John Welley's pits existed for perhaps 100 years after 1453 and in 1458 the churchwardens of St John's, Glastonbury, bought thirteen weys of coal for £4 13s 11d, almost certainly from Stratton. In 1477 six men paid £1 6s 8d rent on a new pit at Stratton.[4]

In the latter half of the eighteenth century,[5] the area was largely owned by the Duchy of Cornwall and was known as the Gore. It was divided into three areas: the Holmes, leased to the Knatchbull family; Barrow, leased by Richard Lansdown on 8 August 1760; and the Gore itself, which was unleased. But by 1783 the Gore was in lease and the Great, Garden and Warkey courses were all being worked by Mr Knatchbull's 'levell'. In the month ending 19 January 1793 the Duchy received £54 11s 5d in freeshare from the Barrow mines, which at a freeshare of one-eighth represents a considerable output.

Moving on from Stratton, the next centre of mining was Holcombe, where there were also numerous shallow workings. As on Stratton Common, however, the identity of the seams worked is largely unknown. Around the village of Holcombe there were several pits—Cole Close, Lantern and Berry, with Duck's Nest Colliery further south. At Dunford's

Farm were several outcrop workings, probably in the Main Coal and Perrink seams. One colliery was still at work in 1824. The only deep mine here, Edford Colliery, closed in 1915, but was outlived by one of the shallow workings owned by the Holcombe Colliery Company.

To the east again, we come to the workings at Kilmersdon Common and the Coleford area. The strata here is much disturbed and only the Perrink and Main Coal seams have been identified. One of the most noted undertakings here worked these seams; this was the Coal Barton pit, sunk some way south of the Anchor Inn at Coleford in a field known as Sheere's Close.[6] In 1829 the concern was rated at £129 and in 1842 there were about 100 people at work there. The pit finally closed down in the 1850s.

To the north-east of Coleford Village were a number of pits. The Ringing Bell group comprised several shafts: Ringing Pit was about 360ft deep and worked detached pieces of nearly vertical coal from the Perrink and Main Coal seams; Middle Ringing Pit lay a few yards to the east and was probably of a similar depth; and New Ringing Pit, perhaps one of these two, was at work by 1824. In 1829 the group was valued at £50. The workings were abandoned about 1830 and in 1831 were said to be in a 'ruinous state', because of which, on 13 October 1831, the Kilmersdon Vestry reduced the poor rate levy. To the south lay Moon's Pit.

A short way to the east of the Ringing pits were the four shafts of Goodeaves Colliery, near Goodeaves Farm. Goodeaves and Old Goodeaves pits were at work in 1824.

Newbury had a host of small pits, sunk on the Coking Coal and Argyll Drift outcrops. On the steep southern slopes of Stock Hill, above the latter-day Vobster pits, numerous other shafts were sunk. In Melcombe Wood, south-east of Vobster, are a series of outcrops comprising probably the Stone Rag, Main Coal and Perrink seams—together with others—and here again dozens of pits were strung out along the outcrops like beads on a thread. To the immediate south and east of Vobster village there were at least fifty pits and probably as many again whose sites will never be known. Today the valley here is quiet and agricultural, but scattered in secluded places are the traces left by the men who persistently sought coal over the centuries.

Turning northwards, we find that only a few pits were sunk. The geology here is unknown in detail, the exact eastern boundary of the coalfield being indeterminate. Mells was the only recent colliery, but there is one older pit worthy of note—the Bilboa pit near Vobster Cross, which was 240ft deep. A level branch was driven northwards and after it had gone 100yd it was said that the men in the drivage were within hearing of men working in the Dunny Drift seam at Upper Catch pit. The Catch group comprised several shafts that were closed early in the nineteenth century; in 1874 it was said that they were at work within living memory.

THE NEWBURY RAILWAY
The Newbury Railway, which connected with the broad-gauge GWR Frome–Radstock line, was promoted by the Westbury Iron Co to serve its Newbury Colliery. The branch was built without a formal agreement with the GWR, so the exact dates of construction are unknown. It is believed that the line was opened about 1857 (certainly by 1864) and it was, of course, also broad gauge. A narrow-gauge tramway was laid to serve the Vobster collieries and carry their produce to the railway.

The new line proved an immediate stimulus to the coalowners and three new pits—Mells, Breach and Mackintosh—were sunk shortly after its opening. The railway was laid on land leased from the Rev J. S. Hippisley Horner by the Westbury Iron Co Ltd, W. B. Naish, John Rees-Mogg, Charles Hollwey, Stephen Steeds, Thomas Pilditch and G. C. Greenwell. It is interesting to note the number of coalowners from the Radstock area who were concerned in the railway. Greenwell, who discovered iron at Westbury, was deeply involved in the iron company, for which he received a strong reprimand from the Waldegraves. In practice, the railway was operated by the Mells Siding Committee, made up of representatives of each user, which apportioned the maintenance costs between users. In due course it was converted to standard gauge.

Horses were used to work traffic at first, but were super-seded by locomotives. Each firm using the line appears to have operated its own traffic. Newbury Colliery had a locomotive by 1910, bought from Avonmouth Docks. It was damaged in an accident and a replacement was hired from the GWR; but shortly afterwards the colliery purchased another locomotive from Avonmouth. By 1922, this locomotive doubtless shunted Mells Colliery and, after Newbury closed in 1927, was prob-ably transferred to Mells.

The construction of the railway opened up a large area of limestone at Vobster Cross and its large-scale working prob-ably dates from the opening of the railway. In the 1870s there was a limekiln here,[7] and the quarries passed to John Wain-wright & Co, and then to the Roads Reconstruction group, which used the railway until the quarries closed about 1959.

It is not known for certain whether coal was transhipped to the Newbury Railway via the narrow gauge line from Vob-ster. There were sidings at Vobster Cross, which originally served a coal depot owned by the Newbury Colliery. In 1874 McMurtrie speaks of Bilboa coal depot, at this point, and, pos-sibly, Vobster coal was only brought as far as the depot.

Today, the course of the line is clear for its entire length; the track is still in situ between Mells Road and Vobster Quarry but has been sold for scrap, so its removal cannot be long delayed. Only the junction with the GWR, serving an oil depot, is still in use.

MELLS COLLIERY

This was sunk about 1863, and was still at work in 1874, but had been closed as unprofitable by 1881. Little is known of this period, though an underground explosion occurred about 1865. By 1871 the pit was owned by W. B. Naish and operated jointly with the Vobster collieries. In this year it was described as 'unpromising'; between February 1869 and the end of 1874, 106,428 tons of coal were raised and sold for £49,397, the lowest price per ton of any pit in the area.[8]

On 22 September 1909 a new lease of the colliery was taken

by Horatio Sheppard, Ernest Smith, George Cook and Egbert Spear.[9] Spear was the managing director of Dunkerton Colliery, whereas the others were solicitors, stockbrokers and merchants from London, whose part seems to have been primarily financial. They formed Mells Collieries Ltd, which by 1916 was managed by Charles Heal, former manager at Dunkerton.

The financial position of the colliery was poor from the start; it proved impossible to pay Somerset district wage rates, but the men refused the company's offer to pay them in proportion to the proceeds of the pit.[10] Working conditions, too, were bad. In 1924, the men complained that ventilation was poor, that there was a shortage of timber for roof supports and that the batteries in their safety lamps would not last for a full shift.[11] None of these faults required anything more than money to correct, but this was lacking. When the time came to pay the monthly bills, the management would literally stick a pin in a list until the available cash was spoken for. The problem for the next month was to put off creditors until the time when the random pin might enable them to be paid. In

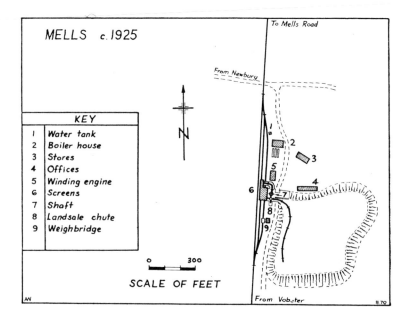

MELLS c. 1925

To Mells Road

From Newbury

N

KEY	
1	Water tank
2	Boiler house
3	Stores
4	Offices
5	Winding engine
6	Screens
7	Shaft
8	Landsale chute
9	Weighbridge

0   300

SCALE OF FEET

From Vobster

February 1928 it was said that the pit had lost £54,000 in the preceding decade. Around 1922, Mells purchased Newbury Colliery and the combined losses for 1922-4 totalled over £69,000. On 23 August 1930, Mells Collieries Ltd was in receivership.[12]

The receiver was unable to sell the pit as a going concern and in 1930 it was taken over by the Mells Estates under Dame F. J. Horner, the hope being expressed that the pit would soon become a prosperous concern.[13] It was worked for some years by the Horner Trustees, but the optimism of 1930 was proved unjustified. In April 1932 the men were asked to co-operate in keeping the pit open, and by June the position was so bad that they were asked to take a 10 per cent wage cut, the owners holding back this proportion of the wages on the promise of paying it when times improved.[14]

The Horner Trustees were succeeded on 15 January 1934 by a new company, Mells Coal Industry Ltd, the directors being Lady Horner, Sir William Haldane, James Allott and C. Russell.[15] S. H. Berry had been appointed manager on 17 May 1933 at a salary of £250pa. He had previously worked at collieries in Earlstown, Lancashire, and later became manager at New Rock.[16]

There was no great improvement under the new company, which made losses totalling £7,000, this figure being kept low by sacking a large number of men. In 1932, only 120 men remained. Attempts were made to keep faith with the men and in March 1934 it was agreed to start repaying the withheld wages, but it proved impossible to find the money. In January 1939 the company went into liquidation and the miners' agent had to apply to the receiver in an attempt to recover what wages he could.[17]

The reason for the liquidation was that, on 5 August 1937, the New Mells Colliery Co Ltd had been registered to take over the colliery by a lease of sixty years from 1 August 1937. The directors were R. A. S. Redmayne, James Allott (of Mells Coal Industry) and P. W. Kemp-Welch. The company had a capital of £25,000 and bought the pit for £16,000. On 18 November 1937 the capital was increased by £80,000, not for improvements at Mells, but for the purchase (on 10 February 1938) of 77,539 shares in William Evans & Co (Old Mills Collieries) Ltd. The directors of Mells assumed similar positions at Old Mills.[18] The combination of pits was curious, considering that Old Mills was a large profit-making concern, whereas New Mells was neither.

Throughout the 1930s the pit had a history of labour trouble. In 1935 the manager accused men of slacking and in the following year they struck work over the introduction of pneumatic picks. This strike lasted for two weeks and was settled on the owners' terms, the places where picks had been used being closed and the men sacked.[19]

An inventory of plant made on 31 October 1936 provides some useful information.[20] The coal winding shaft, deepened to 540ft in 1909, was the western shaft, with a winding engine built in 1893 by R. Nevill & Co Ltd of Llanelly. Rated at 160hp, it was a two-cylinder horizontal engine with cylinders 18in x 42in and separate drums, 10ft in diameter and 2ft 6in wide. The eastern (upcast) shaft, seldom used, was fitted with a converted haulage engine as a winder. Possibly the most intriguing items were three coal-cutting machines lying unused in the stores, doubtless representing an abortive attempt to modernise the workings.

Mells obtained its own locomotive (possibly in 1927) for use on the Newbury Railway. This was an 0-4-0 saddle tank built by Hunslet and was sold for scrap after March 1931 when an 0-6-0 side tank engine, numbered 820 and unofficially christened *Lady Horner,* was bought from the GWR. The colliery owned two motor lorries and seven 8-ton railway trucks to carry its coal.

After the New Mells company took over, the steam winder was replaced by an electric engine, believed to have been the first in Somerset. Unfortunately, being secondhand, it was not really suited to the pit and was wrongly geared; it took forty seconds to wind a full load, against the 24 seconds for the old steam engine. The new owners also modernised in other ways, installing an electric ventilating fan and opening a new canteen, but the results were not encouraging and on 15 January

1943 it was reported that the pit would be closed.[21] The closure was postponed for a while, but there was no increase in output and the pit closed on 30 October 1943.

Today, the site is occupied by a concrete-block making factory and most of the buildings survive intact, despite the removal of machinery in the scrap-metal drives of World War II. The locomotive disappeared during one of these drives, being sold to Cohens for only £100 in February 1945. The capped winding shaft can still be seen, while the screens are in use as a hay barn. The waste tip is the only one in Somerset that is still on fire.

NEWBURY AND MACKINTOSH COLLIERIES

About 1710, Old Newbury Colliery was sunk near the outcrop of the Dungy Drift seam.[22] This colliery was superseded by the new colliery, sunk in the valley north-east of Coleford, which was producing coal by 1799. Good quality coking coal was produced and both this and coke produced in ovens at the pit was sent by road to Westbury Iron Works; at least as early as 1860, the Westbury Iron Co owned the colliery, though the latter continued to trade as the Newbury Coal Co.

To expand operations, the Mackintosh shaft was sunk and

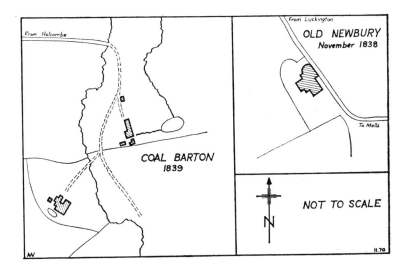

opened in 1867. The shaft was connected underground to Newbury by a small airway, a fan at Mackintosh pithead drawing air down Newbury shaft and out at Mackintosh. The two pits were managed by J. Batey for many years, but it is of interest to note that James McMurtrie took his first post in Somerset as manager of Newbury in April 1862, moving to Radstock in March 1863.

Mackintosh coal was carried on a narrow-gauge (about 2ft 4in) tramway down to Newbury, where it was screened and loaded into railway wagons. To work this tramway, a steam hauling engine was sited at Mackintosh pit top. The opening of Mackintosh had improved Newbury's ventilation but there was still no escape route. Accordingly, a new shaft was sunk near Luckington Cross, work starting on 16 November 1895 and finishing by 4 July 1896. The shaft, variously known as Luckington, Lady Margaret and Margot shaft, was 135ft deep but no winding engine was erected and men had to climb out of the workings via a flight of ladders.

On 30 March 1895 Mackintosh ceased coal winding, a suspension that lasted for five years until trade had improved;[23] Newbury may have closed for a short while also. When they re-opened, it was under the ownership of John Wainwright & Co Ltd, but by April 1912 the owners were Llwydcoed Collieries Ltd, with offices in Eastcheap, London.[24] This involvement of a Welsh firm in the coalfield is strange indeed and it is not known how they came to be involved. Between 1914 and 1917 the pits again changed hands, the new owners being Newbury Collieries Ltd under Sir Richard Paget. The colliery manager after 1917 was T. Twist, formerly of Greyfield Colliery.[25]

In 1919 the ventilation was 'much improved' when a fan was installed at Luckington, which became the main upcast shaft for the two collieries.[26] Mackintosh, however, remained at work only a few months, for, in December 1919, there was a bad accident. The winding rope had been condemned as unsafe but, since no spare was immediately available, it continued in use. On 5 December the rope broke and all winding had to cease. There were pumps at the pit, but these could only cope with the aid of water tanks slung under the cages;

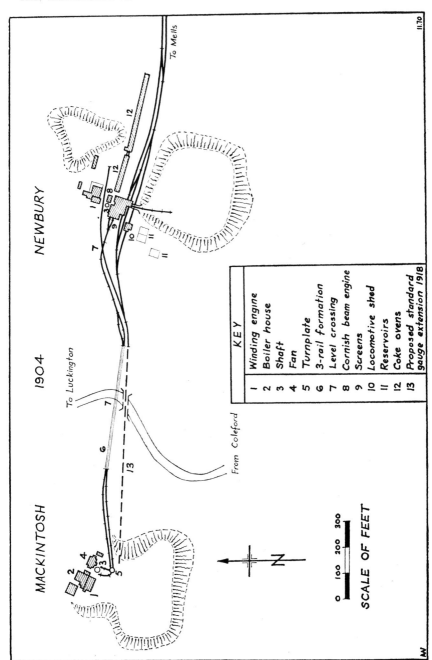

KEY

1 Winding engine
2 Boiler house
3 Shaft
4 Fan
5 Turnplate
6 3-rail formation
7 Level crossing
8 Cornish beam engine
9 Screens
10 Locomotive shed
11 Reservoirs
12 Coke ovens
13 Proposed standard gauge extension 1918

MACKINTOSH   1904   NEWBURY

To Mells

To Luckington

From Coleford

SCALE OF FEET
0   100   200   300

N

since these could no longer be used, the pit began to flood and was permanently closed.[27] The unfortunate pit ponies had grown too large to be brought out of the airway to Newbury and had to be destroyed.

Just before closure, a start had been made on building an extension of the Newbury Railway to Mackintosh, superseding the narrow-gauge line, and the half-completed embankments can be seen to this day.

In the 1920s the pit was producing 40-50,000 tons of coal each year but was in serious financial difficulties.[28] In September 1921, 155 men were sacked to try and cut costs, and the remaining work force of about 270 men offered to take a cut in wages to keep the pit open.[29] Between December 1922 and March 1923 the pit was closed through a breakdown of the pumps.[30] At this period a small subsidy was obtained and used to provide steel headgear, a new steel chimney, a new winding engine and air compressor, and new brick buildings.

After the 1926 strike, the owners decided to cut their losses and start dismantling the pit, but this scheme was postponed. By 24 June 1927 the pit was in the hands of an official receiver and the men were working only on day-to-day contracts. A lengthy report was produced on the pit, setting out the possible developments.[31] There were some 15 million tons of coal reserves but the shaft needed deepening to 1,920ft and Mackintosh needed reopening. The existing machinery was adequate for an output of 2,000 tons per week: the winding engine, built by Wood & Gee, had two 24in x 54in cylinders and was in good order; the Cornish pump had a capacity of 20,000gph at five strokes per minute and, together with a more modern pump, was adequate for the maximum demand of 30,000gph in winter. The report commented that the pit had 'suffered from mismanagement in the past'.

Unfortunately, there was no money to make the necessary improvements and the colliery ceased coal winding on August Bank Holiday 1927; pumping was continued but on 6 August, 'there is no certainty that this will continue' and the men, when they reported for work after the holiday, were told that the pit was shut.[32] Sir Frank Beauchamp toyed with the idea of acquiring the pit, and even started negotiations, but then thought better of the idea.[33]

The two collieries lay derelict until 1948 when the Newbury site was taken over by a reconstructed-stone firm, which demolished the headgear and coke ovens in 1950. The winding and pumping engine houses still stand, as do the colliery offices. The track bed of the narrow-gauge line to Mackintosh is now a road, while the site of that pit has largely been levelled. The foundations of the winding engine, the capped shaft, the fan house and fan drifts can still be found. At Luckington, the few surface works were levelled off after World War II and no traces remain.

THE VOBSTER COLLIERIES

The history of these collieries is complex, both because of a lack of information and contradictions in that which exists. The two pits that primarily concern us—Vobster and Breach —were situated in the east of the Nettlebridge Valley, which flanks the northern slopes of the Mendips. Greenwell in 1858 spoke of the 'remarkable contortions' of the coal seams, and McMurtrie said in 1869 that 'we find an amount of confusion and distortion which literally baffles description'. Anstie said, 'it is marvellous that works can be carried on here under the united disadvantages of broken strata and dangerous firedamp'.

Because the seams were often vertical, the coal was worked in a manner resembling stoping in lead mines. The men would hack away the coal above their heads and then place timbers across to support the 'walls' (actually the roof and floor) of the seam. Standing on their timber, the miners would then again attack the coal overhead, so moving up the seam.

Firedamp was a hazard. McMurtrie said that the seams were 'as fiery as any in England', and the danger was so prevalent that, even in the 1600s, the coal masters provided medical treatment for men burnt in gas explosions. There were many of these: in December 1773 four men were killed at one of the pits when 'a vapourous damp suddenly broke forth'; and in 1800 eleven men were killed in an explosion at Old Breach.[34]

There were many small pits known under the general heading 'Vobster', so it is not always certain which one is meant by a particular reference.

Vobster Colliery

This was sunk at an unknown date some 300yd south-west of Vobster Inn and had three shafts: north and south winding shafts, and a pumping shaft still further north.[35] There was a steam winding engine at the pithead, but pumping was by waterwheels. Seams worked were the Perrink, Stone Rag, Callows or Main, and Firestone, all of which were violently broken and distorted. One branch in the Stone Rag ran westwards for 750yd, and it was to this branch that Breach Pit was sunk in 1860-1.

Breach Colliery

'Vobster New Pit' was sunk 750yd to the west of the 'old pits' to connect with an existing main branch at a depth of 606ft. The contractor agreed to sink the shaft at £4 15s 0d per fathom for the first 50 fathoms, and then at £10 per fathom for the remaining distance. Work began on 23 April 1860 and the connection was made on 27 May 1861.[36] The 'old pits' referred to are presumably the Vobster Colliery and thus 'Vobster New Pit' is clearly Breach. There was a second shaft at Breach, sunk at a later date. It appears that, though the connection was made at 606ft, the shaft was continued to a depth of either 720ft or 867ft.

Breach was well equipped. On 26 July 1861 Paulton Foundry supplied the Vobster Coal Co with two wrought-iron cages, presumably for use at Breach. Two ranks of coke ovens were built by 1867.

There is other information, but it is not known to which pit it refers. The Vobster Coal Co took delivery of four new ends for 6ft diameter boilers in 1863 and in 1865 a winding engine boiler was repaired.[37] Probably both pits had a steam winder, but each used waterwheels for pumping. In February 1868 a new waterwheel costing £75 was bought,[38] Vobster probably being the last pit in Somerset to use such wheels as a

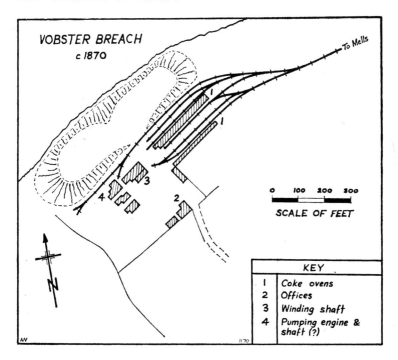

source of power.

The story of these two pits, therefore, is incomplete in many important respects; even the owners are anonymous, though William Beachim and W. B. Naish were involved. The closure dates are similarly inconclusive. One source states that Vobster closed in 1875 and Breach before 1874.[39] However, both pits were working up to 1874, and probably closed at the same time. By 1870 they were owned by the Vobster & Mells Coal Co, as was Mells Colliery, and both pits at Vobster remained at work during the 1874 strike. The output figures for the two pits between February 1869 and 31 December 1874 are as follows:[40]

	Tons	Sold for (£)	Price per ton
Coal	27,999	17,750	12s 8d
Coke	58,722	60,567	20s 7½d

These figures are of interest since they show the importance of coke production at Vobster and Breach; they also suggest that the pits were working into 1875, though they doubtless closed soon afterwards.

We may also mention Vobster Old and Old Breach pits, the location of the latter being unknown; an undated reference mentions that there were four water mills at the pit but they proved inadequate so that 'Mr Sallmon . . . was forced to quit the work'. Vobster Old was sunk 275yd to the east of Vobster Colliery to work an unnamed seam; and the 1773 explosion may have occurred in this pit.

The only remaining trace of Vobster Old is a small dirt tip. The site of Breach, though very marshy, is still clear, with the coke ovens and crumbling chimney, heapstead and outbuildings visible. The track bed of the tramway to Bilboa is open throughout its entire length. Vobster Colliery is more overgrown than Breach, but the foundations of several buildings remain, as does the ditch that carried water to the wheels. The most obvious relic is one of the shafts, nearly filled up, but with a piece of pipe protruding from it; the shaft is stone-lined and still in a fair state of repair.

EDFORD COLLIERY

Sunk before 1863 (probably in the late 1850s), this colliery escaped the notice of contemporary writers until Anstie said in 1873 that it was then working 'very broken ground'. At least as early as 1887 the pit was owned by Howard James Ridler of Flint House, trading as the Edford Colliery Co.[41] By 1914, Ridler had formed the Edford Colliery Co Ltd, which worked the pit up to closure.

The two shafts lay on an east-west line. In later years, a single two-deck cage was wound in each shaft, but when only the eastern shaft was used for winding a balance weight was worked in the other. This was also the upcast shaft, having a fire at the bottom and a brick 'chimney' round its mouth.

Between the two shafts were the winding engine and a Lancashire boiler. The engine had a single cylinder, 18in x 42in, and was geared 3 : 1, working at a pressure of 40psi. In April

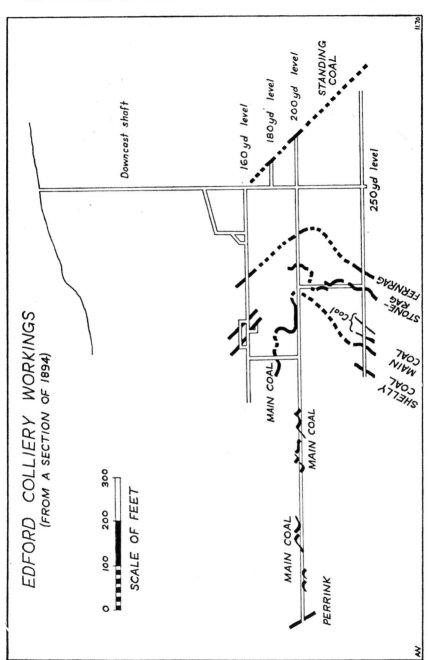

EDFORD COLLIERY WORKINGS
(FROM A SECTION OF 1894)

SCALE OF FEET

0   100   200   300

Downcast shaft

160 yd level
180 yd level
200 yd level
STANDING COAL
250 yd level

MAIN COAL

MAIN COAL

MAIN COAL

MAIN COAL

MAIN COAL

PERRINK

FERNPAG
STONE-RAG
MAIN COAL
SHELLY COAL
Coal

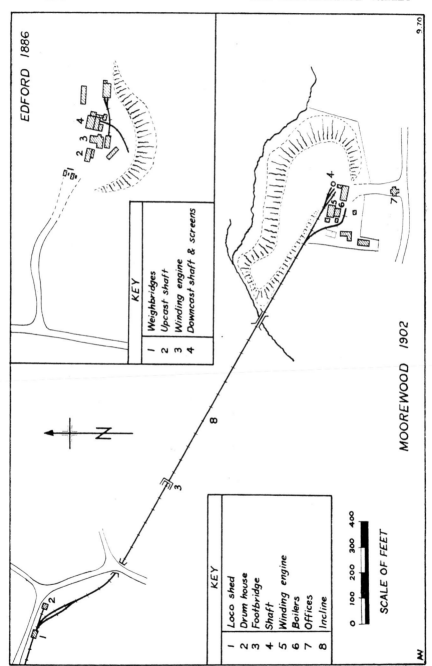

EDFORD 1886

9.70

KEY

1 Weighbridges
2 Upcast shaft
3 Winding engine
4 Downcast shaft & screens

MOOREWOOD 1902

N

KEY

1 Loco shed
2 Drum house
3 Footbridge
4 Shaft
5 Winding engine
6 Boilers
7 Offices
8 Incline

0   100   200   300   400

SCALE OF FEET

1864 a new weighbridge was supplied for £60; this was for road traffic, the sole means of coal disposal, on which horses and carts—and, later, traction engines—were employed.[42]

In common with other pits in the Mendips, Edford had to contend with very poor underground conditions. On 22 February 1886 there was an explosion that killed two men and set fire to part of the workings, and as a result the lower part of the shaft had to be sealed off.

There were also coke ovens at the pit, which built up a good trade in foundry coke. In 1887, coke and coal was taken 4 miles to Radstock station for rail despatch. Ridler was one of the most adventurous colliery owners in Somerset: at the same period he had a coal-washing plant installed, and in 1881 his pit made briquettes of patent fuel and sold them for 11s 8d per ton.[43] None of this could keep the pit at work, however, and it closed down soon after 3 July 1915.

The site is today occupied by a concrete-block factory, but many of the original buildings can still be seen. It is a little strange that Ridler's name occurs nowhere else in connection with collieries—the isolation of this little pit was obviously very complete.

THE HOLCOMBE COLLIERIES

These were a small group started by the Gilson family. A number of drifts and trial shafts were put down, these showing that Holcombe had been fully explored by miners of past centuries. The first drift was put down at Knight's Hill quarry about 1914 and four drifts, Nos 1, 2, 4 and 5, were eventually driven. Only about six men were employed, and work ceased on 19 May 1920. The Holcombe Colliery Co (which was prosperous enough to have its own headed notepaper!) was dissolved in December of that year.[44]

About 1916 the No 3 drift was driven behind Holcombe Brewery. A steam haulage engine was installed here, but little coal was proved, due to faulty ground, and the site was closed about October 1918.

The third and last site was in Blackpool Wood, work being started during the 1921 strike by eight or ten men. The steam

winch from No 3 drift was transferred here and eventually
about 100 tons of coal were being mined each week after
£30,000 had been spent on development. A large hauling
engine was purchased from a colliery at Bargoed in South
Wales, but was never erected here. On 1 February 1923 the
drift broke into water at a depth of 315ft, and the mine closed
in the following month.

BARLAKE COLLIERY

This was sunk before 1819 by Sir John Hippisley, J. S. Hippisley, Uriah and George Messiter and Thomas Davis.[45] By 1825,
there was a steam engine at the pit, though whether for winding or pumping is unknown.[46] In the year ending 30 May
1820, coal worth £1,600 was found and Sir John applied un-
successfully to the lessors for permission to make a road to
carry the produce away. In the year to September 1821, £2,360
was realised from coal sales, an excellent result for the period.[47]
Today, apart from the small dirt tip, nothing remains; the pit
was shut by 1870, and probably about forty years earlier.

PITCOT COLLIERY

Although sunk by 1750, nothing is known of this pit until the
1780s. In the eight years to 30 September 1788, coal worth
£8,845 was produced.[48] The pit was then owned by the Knatchbull family; up to 1787, Captain Knatchbull was the owner,
but his wife Judith held the work in the following year. In
February 1786 it was said that the colliery was unlikely to last
for more than two years and a new colliery was proposed; but
this was not built and Pitcot was developed. Knatchbull considered that, if he erected a 'Fire Engine &c', the result would
be 'one of the Compleatest Coal Works in all the Country'.
This was an extravagant claim, but nonetheless Pitcot was
clearly a profitable pit at the time.

The colliery is believed to have been still at work in 1824,
though a closure date of 1810 has been suggested; it was certainly closed by 1863. There are no remains today other than
the stonework of the older shaft by the road, surrounded by
fields containing numerous unattributable dirt tips.

OLD ROCK COLLIERY

This was financed by Jacob Mogg in 1786, which appears to be the date of sinking.[49] The pit was leased by Mogg, Henry Hippisley Coxe and another man. Coxe took a lease of the colliery—and of the Manor of Stratton—on 10 October 1791, one of the conditions being that he drove a drainage level (the Benter level) to enable the colliery to be properly worked. Coxe may have begun the level in 1789 and it was certainly in use by 1809. The freeshare rate was probably one-tenth to the Duchy of Cornwall, which received £3,779 between 1792 and 1818.[50]

There is considerable confusion as to the number of shafts. The Tun Pit was 240ft deep to the Benter level and was probably only an air shaft; the Engine Pit (presumably for pumping) was 399ft deep; and a third shaft, or perhaps one of the above, was stated to be of 4ft 6in diameter and 711ft 6in deep in 1860.

The pit appears to have been closed by 1863, though in 1869 McMurtrie mentions the 'Old Rock (or present Nettlebridge) Colliery' and calls Nettlebridge Colliery proper by the name of Old Nettlebridge. This implies that Old Rock was reopened under a new name after 1863, possibly in connection with work on Strap Colliery; certainly, the latest reference to Nettlebridge Colliery is October 1863. McMurtrie may be in error, since his 'present Nettlebridge Colliery' on his map actually occupies the position of Sweetleaze Pit. Anstie states that Old Rock was closed by 1873, and today, other than the site of one of the shafts and the tree-planted dirt tip, no trace exists.

NETTLEBRIDGE, SWEETLEAZE AND STRAP COLLIERIES

These formed a closely connected little group and can be considered together. The earliest reference to 'Nettlebridge' is in February 1831, when water from the Benter level found its way into the workings and stopped mining for some while.[51] There were two shafts at the colliery, and a set of coke ovens, at work by 1863.

The colliery suffered more than its fair share of problems, for in 1858-60 there were difficulties with the Benter level, poor ventilation and bad underground roads. In 1858, at the request of the lessees, G. Feare of the Timsbury Collieries, reported on the pit, recommending that it should be developed by driving an incline down to the Garden Course seam, and by sinking a new ventilation shaft. His report was thoroughly critical of the manager, Mr Gould, saying that he appeared to be incapable of working the pit efficiently. Gould was, therefore, replaced by William Treasure, and Feare became surveyor to the colliery.

Treasure did not find his job a bed of roses. He assumed his position in 1859 and found it necessary to warn Feare of threats made by Gould: 'A person . . . told me that he heard George Gould say that you got into Nettlebridge Colliery easier than you will get out of it, with other expressions which I do not like to mention. You may be sure he is no friend of yours'.

On 8 October 1860 Treasure was the victim of what could have been a serious accident: he was wound over the wheel while riding up the shaft hanging on to a loop in the rope, and would have been crushed in the engine drum had not the banksman applied the brake. Treasure's hand was badly cut, and he was 'sorry to say I feel more and more from it'.

Between August and October 1863, less than 250 tons of coal were raised, at a cost of £33. Soon after Treasure's death, about 1870, the pit was closed. The lease, due to expire in December 1877, had been surrendered several years earlier.[52]

The early days of 'Sweetleaze Colliery' are more obscure than those of Nettlebridge, and the pit was closed by 1858 at the latest.[53] In 1859, when water was encroaching on to the Nettlebridge workings, Treasure visited Sweetleaze to measure the water level in the workings. As a preparatory move to sinking Strap Colliery, Sweetleaze was reopened and coal working was resumed. Work on the reopening began in 1861 and a winding engine was installed by William Evans. On 7 September 1862 Evans himself started it up for the first time. The shaft was deepened by 99ft, the work beginning on 16 May

1861 and finishing on 29 August, at a cost of £5 6s 0d per week.[54] Coal was worked fairly regularly in 1863, in conjunction with clearing out the old Edford drainage level, driving a new level to take water into the Benter level, and driving a new air course. The last improvement was certainly needed; on 22 April 1863, Treasure reported that 'The air in the Sweet Leaze Pit has been very bad today, although we keep a big fire in the furnace'. Driving of the various levels was continued throughout the 1860s, but we can now turn to the most important single work—the sinking of the new 'Strap Colliery'.

The Nettlebridge proprietors, represented by Treasure and Feare, instigated the sinking of Strap, or Downside Colliery as it was otherwise known. James Chivers, the head overseer at Nettlebridge, engaged the sinkers and work began in 1862. Sinking was very slow; on 25 June 1862, the shaft had reached 'the bottom of the Strap Pit, which was formerly sunk', and was then at a depth of 162ft. This suggests that the pit was sunk on the site of an old working. By May 1863, the shaft was 205ft deep and had reached the Old Rock level, where the sinking was to be of 14ft 6in diameter, or 10ft 4in diameter inside the walling. Work proceeded until October, when the sinkers, not satisfied with their money, left the work. They were being paid £7 per fathom, which worked out at about £3 per week, to be shared between the gang. New sinkers were hired and Treasure commented, somewhat apprehensively, 'we have not been interrupted by the old sinkers yet'.

By March 1868 the sinking had reached 663ft, extremely slow progress, and the Nettlebridge company had run out of money. In 1868, William Evans of Paulton Foundry and Joseph Hill (both of Old Mills Colliery), took over the sinking. Even under their control, work was slow; by April 1871 the pit was 1,000ft deep and Hill estimated that there was another 500ft to go. Mining in the Great Course began by March 1869, and by 1871 150-200 tons per week were being raised. Both Evans and Hill were apprehensive, however, saying that the pit could never pay unless it had a rail connection;[55] Evans in fact only took over the work in the expectation that a railway would be laid. Nonetheless, by 1874, the shaft had reached its final enormous depth of 1,838ft, the deepest shaft in Somerset, and eight major seams of coal had been proved.

Evans' hopes of rail communication were sadly disappointed; the railway never arrived and, despite the immense financial outlay on the pit, it was closed (together with Sweetleaze) on 3 January 1879. Without rail transport, the pit was hopelessly unprofitable and it probably never came into full production. A brick cap was put in the shaft and covered over with earth, in case there should ever come a time when the pit could be reopened. All the machinery, and many of the buildings, were removed.

Strap would have become just another derelict colliery had is not been for the NCB, which, eighty years later, took advantage of Evans' foresight and reopened the shaft as the Mendip Colliery. This latter-day history will be dealt with under New Rock Colliery (page 251); suffice to say here that Strap must surely rank with Farmborough as one of the most expensive failures in Somerset mining history.

OLD MOOREWOOD COLLIERY

A colliery was at work at Moorewood in 1824, presumably this one. It had a shaft of 4ft 6in diameter and 365ft deep, cutting six major coal seams. Otherwise, nothing is known about it, except that it was closed in the 1860s.

MOOREWOOD COLLIERY

This shaft was sunk in the 1860-70 period on land owned by the Stock family to work the Old Moorewood seams to a greater depth as well as the lower seams. The colliery experienced difficulties with water and was flooded and closed by 1873. (See map, p 242.)

The sinking was instigated by the Westbury Iron Co, which wished to provide coal additional to that already coming from its Newbury Colliery, and £7,000 was spent at Moorewood in expectation of the construction of the S & D branch into the Nettlebridge Valley. However, in the words of John Batey, the manager, 'The non-completion of the branch to Downside Colliery . . . affected our welfare at Moorewood'.[56] In 1876 the pit, though flooded, was described as 'suspended', and it appears that no coal was worked up to the closure.

In or about 1909 the colliery was reopened by the Moore-wood Colliery Co Ltd, owned by Sir Frank and Louis Beauchamp and G. Wilfred Haydon, but by 1924 Louis Beauchamp was the sole owner. This reopening was only partial and it was about four years before the colliery came into full production.

To overcome the limitations of road transport, a 2ft-gauge tramway was constructed in 1913-14 from the colliery, up an incline on Stock Hill and then level to the S & D. Here, a tipping dock and standard-gauge sidings were built under an agreement dated 10 December 1913 stating that the colliery was 'about to construct' the tramway. The tubs, carrying an average load of $9\frac{1}{2}$cwt, were hauled up the incline in sets of six by a steam main-and-tail haulage engine sited at the foot of the incline. At the top of the incline, tubs were formed into trains of twelve or eighteen and pulled to the S & D by a locomotive. One of these was an $0-6-0$ saddle tank built by Peckett of Bristol, which was delivered to the colliery on 22 October 1915. There was another six-coupled locomotive, plus an $0-4-0$ saddle tank that was used mainly to provide spares for its fellows. This tramway lasted at least until 1925 (probably until 1930), when output was insufficient to make it economical and it was replaced by motor lorry transport.

In 1924 the colliery's output averaged 750 tons per week, produced by 150 men. It was never a very profitable undertaking, and on 26 March 1926 one underground district was stopped because of the poor quality of the coal and seventy-one men were given notice.[57] By the end of the decade it was clear that the pit was in a hopeless position. In December 1930 output had fallen to 600 tons per week, and at Christmas 1931 the Perrink seam was closed due to flooding and more men lost their jobs. In January 1932 there were only seventy employees, and by May 1932 forty of these were under notice because, it was said, of falling output and surface reorganisation.[58] On or about 7 December 1932 the pit was closed for good.

The remains of the pithead are almost complete, for apart

from removal of machinery no demolition has been undertaken. The brick chimney is a landmark for miles around and one can still see the sites of the two boilers at its foot. All the buildings are still standing and in a fair state of preservation; the track bed of the tramway, apart from the incline, is still traceable. The tipping dock beside the S & D still exists, and the position of the sidings is clearly marked. After closure of the tramway, these sidings were retained until 1964 to store empty stone wagons from Emborough quarries.

CHARMBOROUGH COLLIERY

This drift mine was the last new colliery to be opened in Somerset, and had a most unfortunate history. Owned by Charmborough Collieries Ltd, the directors were Ralph and Gilbert Beauchamp, with E. H. Staples as geological adviser.

There were three drifts in all, sunk in an area where little mining had previously occurred. The coaling drift was 8ft in diameter and 1,650ft long, dipping in the coal at 1 in 1. There were two other ventilation drifts, one being known as the Hamworthy Slant. Land was leased from Lord Hylton and work began in 1932, the first coal being won from the No 1 seam in March 1933. In this year, under the Somerset District (Coal Mines) Scheme of 1930, the pit was assigned a production quota of 1,746 tons per half year, but the actual output between 1 April and 16 September 1933 was only 59 tons and coal landing ceased until September 1935. Flooding and geological difficulties had greatly hindered the work.[59] In 1939, development was still proceeding but more slowly than had been hoped; £15,000 had then been expended for a total output of less than 8,000 tons, so it is unlikely that any profit was made.[60]

The pit was laid out on modern and spacious lines. Dirt from the drift was used to construct the heapstead, supported by a retaining wall. Tubs of coal were hauled out of the mine by an electric hauler, detached from the rope and pushed by hand to the retaining wall for tipping. At the entrance to the pit yard was an office and weighbridge, coal being disposed of entirely by road.

Following a series of labour troubles, the fifteen men employed ceased work on 2 July 1938 following a reduction in their free-coal allowance from 3cwt to 2cwt per week. The strike lasted for nine weeks, and negotiations were still in progress in January 1939.

After this, when geological problems had been overcome, the labour force was increased to forty-five men by the end of 1940. This had dropped to thirty-one on 26 September 1941 when the colliery was given a production target of 78 tons per week. Even this modest figure was not attained in this year, but production averaged 100 tons per week in 1942, and by 1946 was nearly 160 tons; in this year, the output of 7,833 tons was the highest ever recorded.

On 1 January 1947 the colliery was taken over by the NCB and was closed on 2 August 1947. Charmborough thus had the distinction of being the last pit to be opened in Somerset and the first to be closed by the NCB. In 1950 the owners received £12,532 as compensation for nationalisation, but in the previous year the machinery had been removed and the tip bulldozed over the drift mouth. Today, little remains other than the foundations of the hauling engine, the retaining wall and a few of the buildings, which have been incorporated into a farmyard.

NEW ROCK COLLIERY

New Rock Colliery, though it was the site of the latest and probably the last big mining development that Somerset will ever see, remained relatively unnoticed outside the area. Its clousure in 1968 marked the end of mining in the lower coal seams and the end of mining in the area of Somerset in which it had started.

It is fairly certain that the colliery was sunk in 1819. On 27 November 1819 William Day was granted a lease by Hubert Day.[61] Hubert Day's will, made on 20 June 1822 and instrumented after his death in 1827, bequeathed the major share of the financial benefits resulting from ownership of the land on which the colliery stood to George Bragge Prouse and John Hubert Hunt, who became the lessors of the 1819 lease, but a part share also went to the trustees of the will, Mr and Mrs Church. Their son, the Rev William Higginson Montague Church, inherited the land on the death of his mother in 1844.

Another share in the land went to the Rev W. S. Langdale and Mrs Mary Hepburn, who sold it to William Montriou of Calu, in the French Republic. Montriou mortgaged this land to Church, who eventually held all the land concerned with the colliery and received the financial benefits of the works. In Church's own words, 'the working of the said mines under the lease of 27 November 1819 was very unsuccessful' and in or about 1858 the lease was determined, the workings were stopped and did not immediately restart. One reason for this may have been the death of the proprietor of the mine, William Day, in December 1856, for up to 1858, when the mine was closed, no new operators are known. Before very long, however, the pit was reopened under the ownership of John Plummer, William Marchant and James Bryant, who obtained from Church a 21 year lease of the pit, running from 9 February 1859.

By 15 September 1877 the rights of the colliery were vested in John Plummer (who appears to have been the principal adventurer), Mercy Bryant (widow of James Bryant), Jonas Cook and John George Cook. On this date, Church agreed to terminate the 1859 lease and grant a new one for a period of 40 years, giving the lessees rights to work all seams of coal. The main clause in this lease was the requirement that the lessees were bound, within seven years from 9 February 1877, to sink a new shaft to a depth of at least 1,800ft. In 1882, the requirement to sink a new shaft was waived and in lieu it was agreed that the existing shafts should be deepened by 31 December 1885 at the latest. A new lease to this effect was signed on 9 August 1882.

As regards the trading title of the colliery, an indenture of 1 July 1886 states that the pit was trading as the New Rock Colliery Company and the partners on this date were Richard and Mercy Stock, Henry King and John Cook. The reason for this indenture was that, in 1886, the colliery was bought by

Frederick Spencer of Oakhill, who asked for the lease to be transferred to him for the residue of its term. It was noted at this time that the shafts had not been deepened as had been required.

Spencer, on receiving the transferred lease, viewed with some concern the provision requiring him to deepen the shafts, and, wishing to avoid the considerable expense that would be incurred, produced alternative plans (on 6 April 1887). He proposed to drive an incline from pit bottom in the Garden Course seam and erect at its head an engine working on compressed air supplied from the surface 'for hauling coal from the deep'. The reaction of the lessors was that they would agree to this only if Spencer submitted the proposals to two independent mining experts for approval. If they concurred then the work had to start within three months; if not, then the shafts were to be deepened as originally planned. The experts must have agreed that Spencer's plans would not reduce the lessors' benefits from the development of the pit, for the roads were driven as Spencer had proposed.

It was rather unfortunate that Spencer avoided the expense of deepening the shafts, for the incline proved to be a major limiting factor in the growth of the colliery. If the shafts had been deepened as originally intended by the lessors, then the later history of New Rock might have been very different.

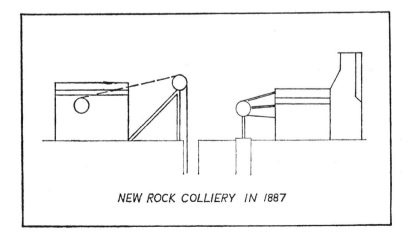

NEW ROCK COLLIERY IN 1887

Spencer began to improve the method of coal disposal, which up to that time had been only by horse and cart. On 10 September 1915 he obtained an option to build an overhead ropeway from the colliery to Chilcompton Station to expedite the carriage of coal thereto. The last landowner concerned gave him permission in 1919 to construct this ropeway but it was never built. To cope with the increased road traffic, a private siding at Chilcompton was laid under an agreement dated 31 July 1911.

Spencer died on 3 August 1918 and the executors of his will continued to work the colliery. During 1920 they obtained licences to assign the various leases to Louis B. Beauchamp who had bought the colliery, the last assignation being 8 December 1920. Guy Beauchamp was also a director, and the family remained the owner of the pit until 1947, the colliery being run as a limited company after 1926.

So far we have been concerned with the lease history of New Rock, which provides a well documented story of the pit's development. Information on the equipment is, unfortunately, rather sparse. As sunk, the pit consisted of a winding shaft and a pumping/upcast shaft, each varying in diameter between 4ft 6in and 4ft 9in. The winding shaft was 1,182ft deep.

It was under Spencer's ownership that real improvements were made, the main work being driving the incline from pit bottom. This incline was a major piece of mining engineering, running downwards for about 650 yd at a mean gradient of 1 in $2\frac{1}{2}$. In 1904 a power house was built to generate electricity, possibly for the installation of electric fan ventilation.

In the winding shaft a single three-deck cage was used, carrying three 10cwt tubs per lift. This might be thought to be very limiting on the pit's output but, though in the twentieth century it was one of the smallest Somerset pits, it had a potential output of 300 tons per day, or about 6,000 tons per month. Output usually fell rather short of this, during 1935, for example, ranging from 3,500 to 5,000 tons per month.[62]

The number of men employed was fairly constant at about 200. In 1937, however, there were 210 men, and it is curious

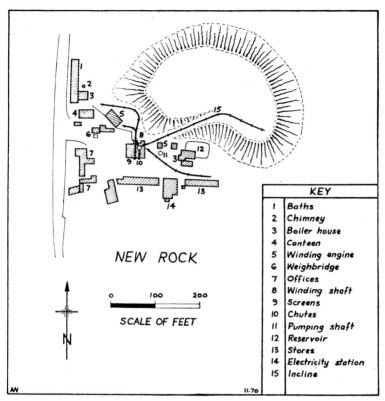

NEW ROCK

SCALE OF FEET

	KEY
1	Baths
2	Chimney
3	Boiler house
4	Canteen
5	Winding engine
6	Weighbridge
7	Offices
8	Winding shaft
9	Screens
10	Chutes
11	Pumping shaft
12	Reservoir
13	Stores
14	Electricity station
15	Incline

that out of only 29 non-union men in the coalfield 20 were at New Rock.[63]

Under the National Coal Board in 1947, further improvements were made, notably the installation of an electric winding engine on the pumping shaft. But before continuing with the history, we should consider the 'Mendip Development'— the NCB's plan to overcome the limited capacity of the New Rock shaft and incline and give the pit a new lease of life.[64]

This development was begun under the programme started by the NCB in 1953 of proving the reserves of the coalfield. The programme took the form mainly of putting down boreholes to explore the ground but, in the Mendips, the idea was conceived of draining the old Strap Pit in order to examine its seams and gain a better idea of coal quality than could be obtained from a borehole core.

Exploration began early in 1954; the exact site of the shaft was unknown and it was eventually found by boring. Preliminary digging established that, 27ft from the top of the shaft, a brick and mortar cap had been put in after 1879 and the space above this filled up with earth. On 1 June 1954 authority was given to begin draining the shaft. The cost was estimated at £48,600 and the completion time about 9-12 months.

The first problem was to remove the capping, which eventually had to be blasted away. Underneath, it was found that the shaft had been divided into two for ventilation purposes, and it was necessary to remove this partition as the water level was lowered from its original level of 210ft below the capping. At the end of December 1955, £46,581 had been spent. A submersible electric pump, lowered in the shaft by a portable diesel winding engine, was used to pump out the water, and the shaft bottom was reached in January 1956. The sump was found to be filled up with rubbish, but in the old workings an interesting relic was discovered in the form of a small trolley, running on 'L' plateway, such as had been common in Somerset in the nineteenth century.

Now came the initial assessment. The shaft, which had originally been thought to be about 15ft in diameter, was in fact only 10ft 6in. Furthermore, it had proved impossible to examine any seams, since the shaft was entirely brick lined; nor were the positions of the seams marked in the walling as had been hoped. The scheme thus failed in its initial object, but the outlay was far from wasted.

Two main plans now received consideration. The first, which was rejected, was a scheme to restart mining at Strap and connect the pit to Moorewood Colliery, which would be reopened as the upcast shaft. The second plan was prompted by the 1954 Coal Mines Act, under which the egress at New Rock Colliery would have to be improved. It will be remembered that the New Rock winding shaft was 1,182ft deep and of only 4ft 6in diameter. The upcast shaft was wider (5ft diameter) but only 540ft deep, the intervening distance being travelled by a staple pit and inclined roadways. Because of pipes and cables in the second shaft, only a very small cage could be worked in it and it did, in fact, take six hours to raise the entire underground shift by this emergency route, which made it valueless in the event of any accident to the other shaft. To comply with the Act, there were two courses of action. Either the second shaft could be deepened and improved (estimated cost £43,000) or a second means of egress could be established. The obvious choice was the newly drained Strap Pit, which had been found in good condition despite nearly 80 years of immersion. This alternative, though estimated to cost £5,910 more than the first, was decided upon, probably because the connection that would have to be driven between New Rock and Strap would achieve the hitherto unrealised aim of proving the strata. Authority for this course of action was obtained, therefore, and by August 1957 the connection was established.

At New Rock, if it was difficult to wind men in an emergency, it was equally difficult to wind coal under normal circumstances. In May 1962, all coal was being loaded in the Great Course seam, pulled up a 260yd incline, hauled on the level for 400yd and then hauled up another incline 650yd long before travelling the final 80yd. on the level to reach pit bottom. This complex underground haulage was wasteful and, together with the restrictions imposed by the shaft, limited the colliery to a daily maximum output of 300 tons, worked on two shifts.

It was decided that if the roles of the two shafts were reversed, and Mendip was fitted up to wind all New Rock coal, it would be possible to increase output from the New Rock faces to 90,000 tons a year. The proposal would give Mendip a shaft capacity of 400 tons per shift and have the additional advantage that all the coal could be produced on one shift, thus easing the deteriorating manpower situation.

Nor was this all. To replace the ageing steam winder at New Rock it was proposed to remove the 200hp hauler from the main incline there and modify it for winding in the shaft. Already, to help overcome the labour shortage and increase output, coal ploughs had been introduced at New Rock, the first in March 1962 and the second, a reserve, in July of that

R

year. This development meant that 70,000 tons of coal could be produced each year on the two-shift system. If the disadvantages of coal winding at New Rock could be overcome, the ploughs could also be used to better advantage. This was a scheme prepared on the cheapest and most unambitious lines, which, even so, was estimated to cost £139,659. It was also estimated that the new pit would have a life of thirty-three years, there being about 3 million tons of coal reserves. Application for the necessary capital was made on 17 July 1962 and approved on 3 August, when work was immediately begun.

Nearly all the plant was secondhand, much having been earmarked for some while beforehand. An electric winder came from Vivian Colliery in South Wales, where it had been winding from a depth of 825ft. At Mendip, it would wind from a depth of 1,758ft and lift one tub (12cwt tare and 27cwt capacity) per cage. One point of interest about this winder was that it had a spiral drum, unusual in Somerset, varying from 12ft 6in to 7ft 6in.

Construction on these minimal lines proceeded and it was decided that the first coal would be raised on 23 December 1963. At the pithead there was a small gravity-worked tub circuit, the tubs being lifted up on an automatic hoist and the coal tipped into the preparation plant. The winding engine was housed in a new asbestos-clad building, but the pithead buildings—lamp room, time office and so on—were mainly the original Strap Colliery buildings. The old Strap landsale chutes indeed still survived behind the dirt tip. No improvements were needed at New Rock other than modifications to the pithead baths.

Even when Mendip was fully operational in 1964 the problem of labour shortage was apparent throughout the coalfield, and more especially at New Rock, which was away from the main centres of population. Increasing labour difficulties, coupled with the disadvantages of transporting coal by road, meant that New Rock's future began to look increasingly black. The pit made bad losses in the first months of 1968 and the decision was taken to close the two shafts and cease coal

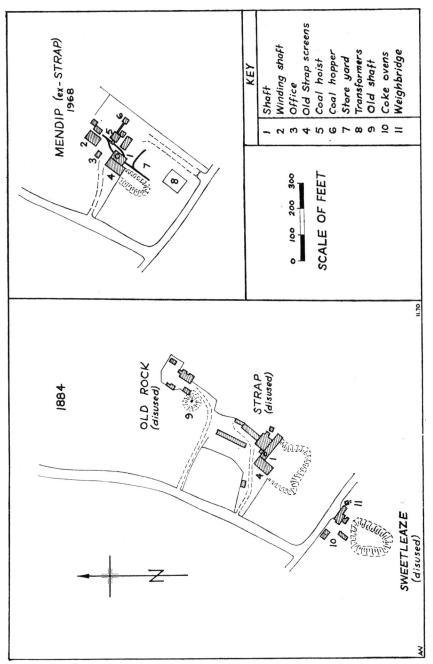

KEY

1	Shaft
2	Winding shaft
3	Office
4	Old Strap screens
5	Coal hoist
6	Coal hopper
7	Store yard
8	Transformers
9	Old shaft
10	Coke ovens
11	Weighbridge

MENDIP (ex-STRAP)
1968

1884

OLD ROCK
(disused)

STRAP
(disused)

SWEETLEAZE
(disused)

SCALE OF FEET

0 100 200 300

N

R*

winding on 28 September 1968. A start was immediately made on salvaging reusable materials, or items with a worthwhile scrap value, and the men were transferred to Kilmersdon and Writhlington to help remedy labour shortages there.

By June 1969 all machinery had been removed from both New Rock and Mendip, and the New Rock shafts had been filled up with dirt from the waste tip. Most buildings at Mendip have been demolished, but the surface at New Rock is still largely intact.

Notes begin on page 271.

SOURCES

Abbreviations used in this section include:

BNHAFC	*Proceedings of the Bath Natural History and Antiquarian Field Club*
BofT	Board of Trade
B & NSR	Bristol & North Somerset Railway
CTR	Calendar of Treasury Records
DofC	Duchy of Cornwall
GWR	Great Western Railway
HLRO	House of Lords Record Office
misc corr	miscellaneous correspondence (of SMA)
NCB	National Coal Board
NEIME	*Transactions of the North of England Institute of Mining Engineers*
S & D	Somerset & Dorset Railway
SANHS	*Proceedings of the Somerset Archaeology and Natural History Society*
SCC	Somerset Coal Canal
SMA	Somerset Miners' Association
SRO	Somerset Record Office
SWIE	*Transactions of the South Wales Institute of Engineers*
Trans	Transactions of the society named
WSWR	Wilts Somerset & Weymouth Railway

BIBLIOGRAPHY

Anstie, J. *The Coal Fields of Gloucestershire and Somerset* (1873)

Atthill, Robin. *Old Mendip*, Dawlish (1964)

Billingsley, John. *General View of the Agriculture of Somerset* (1867)

Buckland, Rev W. and Conybeare, Rev W. D. 'Observations on the South-western Coal-district of England', *Trans Geological Society of London*, 1, series 2 (1824), 210-80

Bulley, John. 'To Mendip for Coal, Part I', SANHS, 97 (1952), 46-78

——'To Mendip for Coal, Part II', SANHS, 98 (1953), 17-45

Clew, K. *The Somersetshire Coal Canal and Railways*, Newton Abbot (1970)

Collinson, Rev J. *The History & Antiquities of the County of Somerset*, Vols 2, 3, Bath (1791)

Galloway, R. L. *Annals of Coal Mining and the Coal Trade* (1898)

——*Annals of Coal Mining and the Coal Trade*, 2nd series (1904)

Gilson, R. G. and Quartley, G. W. 'Some Technical Aspects of the Somersetshire Coal Canal Tramways', *Journal of Industrial Archaeology*, 5 (1968), 140-61

Greenwell, G. C. 'Notes on the Coalfield of East Somerset', NEIME, 2 (1853-4), 251-9

——'On the Southern Portion of the Somersetshire Coalfield', SWIE, 1 (1858), 147-61

——'On the Somersetshire Section of the Bristol Coal-Field', NEIME, 10 (1861), 105-11

——'The South Eastern Portion of the Somersetshire Coal Field', *Trans Manchester Geological Society*, 5, no 3 (1864-5), 34-40

——'On the correlation of the Dover and Somerset Coalfields', *Trans Manchester Geological Society*, 25 (1898), 378-94 and 510-24

——and McMurtrie, J. *On the Radstock Portion of the Somerset Coalfield* (1864)

Hull, E. *The Coalfields of Great Britain* (1861), 75-82

Hylton, Lord. *Notes on the history of the parish of Kilmersdon*, Taunton (1910)

Jenkins, Rhys. 'Jonathan Hornblower and the Compound Engine', *Trans Newcomen Society*, 11 (1930), 138-55

McMurtrie, J. 'The Coalfields of Somersetshire', SANHS, 13 (1865), 16-21

——'Lecture on the Carboniferous Strata of Somersetshire', BNHAFC, 1 (1867-70), 45-60. Read 15 January 1868

——'Faults and contortions in the Somersetshire Coal Field', BNHAFC, 1 (1867-70), 127 49. Read 24 February 1869

——'The Geographical Position of the Carboniferous Formation in Somersetshire', BNHAFC, 2 (1870-3), 454-68. Read 15 January 1873

——'On Certain Areas of Mountain Limestone at Luckington and Vobster in the County of Somerset', BNHAFC, 3 (1873-7), 287-300. Read 9 December 1874

——'The Physical Geology of the Carboniferous Strata of Somerset and associated Formations', SANHS, 21, part 2 (1875), 40-52

——'On the Pumping Arrangements of the Radstock Collieries', SWIE, 11, no 2 (1878)

——'On the Somersetshire Coalfield and the Method of Working Thin Seams in the Radstock District', SWIE, 12, no 5 (1881), 424-54 and 513-24

——'Report of Excursion to Radstock', SANHS, 30 (1884), 85-99

——'Salt Springs in the Coal Measures at Radstock', BNHAFC, 6 (1889), 84-94. Read 10 February 1886

Mines Department. *Catalogue of Abandoned Mines of Somerset* (no date)

Ministry of Fuel and Power. *The Bristol & Somerset Coalfield—Regional Survey Report*, HMSO (1946)

Moore, L. R. and Trueman, A. E. 'The Coal Measures of Bristol and Somerset', *Quarterly Journal of the Geological Society*, 93 (1937), 195-240

—— —— 'The Structure of the Bristol and Somerset Coalfield', *Proceedings of the Geological Association*, 50 (1939), 46-67

—— —— 'The Bristol & Somerset Coalfield with particular reference to the prospects of future development', SWIE, 62 (1942), 180

Morgans, W. *A Survey of the Bristol Coal-Field*, Bristol (1884)

Presto, Jonathan. *Five years of colliery life* (1884)

Richardson, L. 'Section of No 1 Pit, Dunkerton Collieries, Dunkerton, Somerset', SANHS, 70 (1924), 117-21

Staples, E. H. 'Some effects of the Master Folds upon the Structure of the Bristol and Somerset Coalfields', *Trans Federated Institute of Mining Engineers*, 52 (1917), 187-97

Steart, F. A. 'Overthrusts and disturbances in the Braysdown Colliery', *Quarterly Journal of the Geological Society*, 58 (1902), 609-19

Southern, C. 'Use of Steel Props at Kilmersdon Pit', *Proceedings National Association of Colliery Managers*, 30 (1933), 662-71

Warner, Rev R. *A Walk Through some of the Western Counties of England*, Bath (1800)

MANUSCRIPT SOURCES

Anon. *Brief Historical Review, Somerset & Bristol Coalfield* (c 1963), NCB typescript

Beech, H. *Mining Progress Through the Ages* (c 1963), private typescript relating to Norton Hill Colliery

Paulton Foundry ledger; containing details of orders between 1860 and 1870

Radstock notebooks; miscellaneous notes made during 1926 strike, apparently copied from older notebooks now destroyed (NCB records)

Timsbury Minute Books; minute books of the Timsbury Collieries, various dates. In possession of NCB and Bath & Camerton Archaeological Society

Wells, W. C. *Brief Description of the Coalmeasure Structure and Historical Review of the Somerset & Bristol Coalfield,* NCB typescript (1964)

ORIGINAL SOURCES

Beauchamp Records. Leases of New Rock Colliery; miscellaneous papers relating to Somerset Collieries Ltd and family coal interests; minutes of Somerset Coal Owners Association meetings; and other papers of mining interest. Through the courtesy of the executors of the late G. E. L. B. Beauchamp these records have been deposited in the Somerset Record Office

Board of Trade. Company records, sometimes including annual reports of Somerset colliery firms

Duchy of Cornwall. As a major landowner in the coalfield, the Duchy has a large collection of leases, output statistics and correspondence relating to collieries which have worked its coal

House of Lords Record Office. Useful records include the minutes of evidence given by coalowners on the various railway Bills submitted to Parliament

National Coal Board. The Board, apart from material sent to the Somerset Record Office, retains numerous working plans, reports and other data relating to collieries both before and after nationalisation

Somerset Miners Association. The Association's records are housed in the Wills Memorial Library, University of Bristol. They include minute books and numerous correspondence files

Somerset Record Office. At Taunton is housed the largest single collection of material relating to the coalfield. The collection includes documents relating to the Hippisley, Hylton, Rees-Mogg, Samborne, Savage and Waldegrave coal interests, as well as other material

CHAPTER SOURCES

Of necessity, only a skeleton list of sources can be given here. Firstly a sentence may contain facts from half a dozen different sources and it is clearly impossible to list them all. An attempt has been made to list mainly those sources which will provide information additional to that given in the text. Of the sources quoted above, the records of the Duchy of Cornwall, National Coal Board and Somerset Miners' Association are not normally available for public inspection. The Beauchamp, Duchy of Cornwall, National Coal Board and Somerset Miners' Association material is not indexed and it is, therefore, referred to below in only the most general terms. The Somerset Record Office collection is comprehensively catalogued.

Unless otherwise stated, all information on shaft depths and diameters, seams worked, etc, is from NCB records. Similarly, all information on railway sidings, etc, is from the records of British Railways, unless otherwise stated.

CHAPTER 1

1 Galloway (1904), 181
2 Morgans (1884)
3 Galloway (1898), 6
4 CTR, numerous references after 1660
5 Bulley (1952), 46
6 Clew, K. R. *The Somersetshire Coal Canal*
7 Report to Lord Hylton of Ammerdown
8 Morgans (1884)
9 Bulley (1952), 58
10 Hull (1861)
11 HM Inspector of Mines, various annual reports
12 Beauchamp records
13 Report (1946), Ministry of Fuel and Power
14 SMA, misc corr
15 Williams, J. E. *The Derbyshire Miners* (1962), 566, 567
16 Beauchamp records
17 Ibid, Somerset Coal Owners' Association minutes
18 SMA, misc corr
19 Beauchamp records, Somerset Coal Owners' Association minutes
20 Report (1946), Ministry of Fuel and Power
21 Wells (1964), NCB typescript
22 NCB records
23 NCB records
24 Bulley (1953), 48
25 Anon, *Brief Historical Review, Somerset and Bristol Coalfield* (NCB typescript)
26 SMA, misc corr
27 *Western Daily Press*, 12 August 1926
28 SMA, misc corr
29 Report (1946), Ministry of Fuel and Power
30 Ibid

CHAPTER 2

Geological information is taken from the sources listed in the Bibliography

1 Bulley (1952), 63
2 Bulley (1952), 65
3 Galloway (1898)
4 NCB records
5 Greenwell & McMurtrie (1864)
6 Greenwell & McMurtrie (1864)
7 Radstock notebooks
8 Greenwell & McMurtrie (1864)
9 Greenwell & McMurtrie (1864)
10 McMurtrie (1881) and Presto (1884)
11 *Report of the Guss Committee*, HMSO (1928) Cmd 3200

CHAPTER 3
1 SRO, DD/RM 9
2 Ibid, lease 7 August 1855
3 Ibid, mortgage 17 May 1853
4 SRO, DD/RM 9
5 SRO, Bishop Sutton minute books
6 SMA, misc corr
7 Ibid
8 Ibid
9 HM Inspector of Mines, annual reports
10 *Western Daily Press*, 6 January 1905
11 SMA, misc corr
12 Avonside Engine Co, order books
13 SMA, minute, 5 September 1922
14 NCB records, report 2 April 1914 by J. Fox Tallis
15 NCB records
16 BofT, company records, diss 173001
17 Ibid
18 SMA, minute 16 June 1922
19 SMA, minute 23 August 1929
20 SMA, minute 5 February 1932
21 BofT, company records, diss 173001
22 Ibid
23 Buckland & Conybeare (1824) and NCB records
24 Timsbury minute books and NCB records
25 BofT, company records, 907337
26 SRO, DD/RM 22, letter to Edward Popham

CHAPTER 4
1 SRO, Clutton tithe map (1838)
2 Paulton Foundry ledger
3 HM Inspector of Mines, report (1887)
4 Diaries of J. H. Cook
5 Information on Greyfield is from SRO, DD/RM 18 unless otherwise
  stated
6 SRO, DD/RM 25

7 Paulton Foundry ledger
8 Paulton Foundry ledger
9 Bath reference library, Warwick estate book
10 Industrial Railway Society records
11 Information courtesy K. P. Plant
12 SMA, misc corr
13 Diaries of J. H. Cook
14 SMA, misc corr
15 Ibid
16 Ibid
17 Ibid, and minute books (various dates)
18 NCB records
19 SMA, misc corr

CHAPTER 5

Note: information in this chapter comes from Timsbury Minute Books
unless otherwise stated
1 HLRO, minutes of evidence on B & NSR Bill, Vol 7 Grp B5 (1871),
  evidence of S. S. P. Samborne
2 Information courtesy Miss J. Saunders
3 Anstie (1873)
4 Greenwell & McMurtrie (1864)
5 Collinson (1791)
6 Timsbury Minute Books
7 SRO, DD/NCB C/1499/51
8 SRO, DD/NCB C/1499/51
9 Timsbury Minute Books
10 SRO, DD/RM 17 and DD/RM 23
11 SRO, DD/RM 17
12 SRO, DD/RM 22
13 Bath Reference Library, map of the area (no date)
14 SRO, DD/RM 17
15 SRO, DD/PL C/463/31
16 Bulley (1952), 75
17 SRO, DD/RM 19
18 Bulley (1952), 49
19 SRO, DD/NCB C/1499/54
20 *Bristol Mercury*, 27 July 1872
21 SRO, DD/RM 22

CHAPTER 6

Information in this chapter is from Timsbury Minute Books unless
otherwise stated
1 SRO, DD/NCB C/1499/56
2 *Bristol Observer*, 9 February 1895
3 SMA, minute 28 March 1911
4 SMA, minutes 17 January 1912 and 19 February 1912
5 *Keene's Bath Journal*, 4 April 1874
6 Radstock notebooks

7 SRO, DD/NCB C/1499/56
8 Radstock notebooks
9 Radstock notebooks
10 *Bristol Observer*, 18 November 1893
11 Beauchamp records, Camerton Royalty Books
12 Beauchamp records

CHAPTER 7
1 Radstock notebooks
2 SRO, DD/NCB C/1499/61
3 NCB records
4 SMA, minute 19 October 1903
5 *Bath Chronicle*, 4 April 1907
6 *Western Daily Press*, issues throughout this period
7 SMA, minute 25 January 1909
8 SMA, misc corr
9 *Western Daily Press*, 2 June 1925
10 Beauchamp records
11 SMA, misc corr
12 Beauchamp records
13 NCB records
14 Priston history from information courtesy of W. Vaughan-Jenkins, and Beauchamp records

CHAPTER 8
1 Information courtesy William Rees-Mogg
2 *Calendar of Treasury Records*, various references between 1660 and 1696
3 DofC records; these have supplied all the lease history of Farrington Colliery
4 Beauchamp records
5 Information courtesy K. P. Plant
6 Industrial Railway Society records
7 *Western Daily Press*, 13 October 1921
8 Paulton Foundry ledger
9 NCB, James Allott's report (1946)
10 Bulley (1952), 65
11 SMA records
12 NCB records
13 NCB, James Allott's report (1946)
14 BofT, company records, diss 222260
15 BofT, company records, diss 222260
16 SMA, minute 1 January 1932
17 SMA, minute 22 December 1944
18 *Western Morning News & Daily Gazette*, 18 July 1934

CHAPTER 9
1 SRO, DD/RM 22
2 SRO, DD/RM 22

3 SRO, DD/MGG, C/1299/2
4 HM Inspector of Mines, reports 1887, 1893,
5 Billingsley (1798), 27
6 SRO, DD/RM 22
7 SRO, DD/WG 32
8 Beauchamp records
9 SRO, Rennie's plan of SCC (1793)
10 SMA, misc corr
11 HLRO, minutes of evidence on B & NSR Bill, Vol 5 Grp B3 (1870), evidence of Charles Hollwey
12 SRO, DD/WG 32, Greenwell's evidence on Radstock & Keynsham Railway
13 SRO, DD/WG 35
14 Beauchamp records
15 SRO, DD/RM 22, DD/RM 26; and DofC records
16 Radstock notebooks
17 Greenwell & McMurtrie (1864)
18 SRO, DD/WG 32
19 SRO, DD/RM 26
20 SRO, DD/RM 26
21 SRO, DD/RM 26

CHAPTER 10
Information largely from SRO, DD/WG; leases, annual reports and correspondence. Sources other than this are given below, though in many cases the information is duplicated in DD/WG
1 SRO, DD/WG 32
2 SRO, DD/NCB C/1449/75
3 SRO, DD/RM 22
4 SRO, DD/WG 32
5 HM Inspector of Mines, annual reports
6 SMA, minute 14 January 1920
7 SMA, minute 14 February 1920
8 *Somerset Guardian*, 9 March 1920
9 SMA, minute 6 March 1920
10 SMA, minute 18 September 1920
11 SRO, DD/WG 31
12 SMA, minute 26 November 1909
13 SRO, DD/WG 32
14 SRO, DD/WG 32; McMurtrie's evidence on B & NSR Bill
15 SRO, DD/WG 32
16 SRO, DD/WG 32
17 SMA, minute 4 February 1922

CHAPTER 11
1 BofT, company records, diss 51998
2 NCB records
3 Radstock notebooks
4 SRO, DD/WG 32, letter SCC to J. Parfitt, 9 November 1854
   s

5 SRO, DD/WG 35
6 SMA, minute 28 January 1898
7 Radstock notebooks
8 SMA, minute 25 February 1912
9 SRO, DD/RM 22
10 NCB records
11 SRO, DD/WG 32, Waite's evidence on Radstock & Keynsham Railway Bill (1862)
12 SRO, DD/WG 32
13 NCB records
14 SRO, DD/WG 31, statement by William Steart
15 HLRO, minutes of evidence on S & D Bill, Vol 45 Grp S2 (1871)
16 Ibid, Vol 44 Grp S1 (1871), evidence of Alban Chivers
17 Beauchamp records
18 Beauchamp records, 1946 report on Braysdown
19 NCB records
20 SMA, misc corr
21 NCB records
22 SMA, book of press cuttings, 23 June 1864
23 SRO, DD/WG 32
24 HLRO, minutes of evidence on S & D Bill, Vol 44 Grp S1 (1871), evidence of W. B. Naish
25 NCB records
26 SMA, minute 20 March 1931
27 Information courtesy of Lord Hylton of Ammerdown
28 NCB records
29 BofT, company records, diss 51998
30 Southern, C. 'Use of Steel Props at Kilmersdon Pit' (1933)
31 Report to Lord Hylton (1939)
32 NCB records
33 Ibid
34 Ibid

CHAPTER 12
1 Kelly's *Directory of Bristol & Somerset* (1866)
2 SRO, DD/WG 31
3 SRO, DD/NCB C/1499/65, partnership agreement 21 December 1904
4 SRO, DD/NCB C/1499/75
5 BofT, company records, diss 208648; and Beauchamp records
6 BofT, company records, diss 208648
7 Beauchamp records
8 Ibid
9 Ibid
10 SMA, misc corr
11 Beauchamp records
12 *Who's Who in Somerset* (1934)
13 SRO, Midsomer Norton tithe map, 15 July 1839
14 SRO, Savage deeds 59

15 Ibid
16 Ibid; and Savage deeds 78
17 *Western Daily Press,* 11 April 1908
18 NCB records
19 NCB records

CHAPTER 13
 1 SRO, DD/HI 3; eg lease 29 September 1756 from Lord Weymouth
 2 SRO, DD/HI 4
 3 Anon, *A Compleat History of Somersetshire* (1742), 74
 4 Bulley (1953), 17
 5 DofC records
 6 SRO, Kilmersdon tithe book, 28 August 1838
 7 McMurtrie (1874)
 8 SRO, DD/WG 35
 9 Mells deeds, courtesy Messrs Haldane & McLaren, W. S.
10 SMA, minute 10 September 1921
11 SMA, misc corr
12 SMA, misc corr
13 SMA, minute 23 August 1930
14 SMA, misc corr
15 BofT, company records, diss 330486
16 Mells deeds
17 SMA, minute 27 January 1939
18 BofT, company records, diss 330486
19 SMA, minutes 16 and 25 September 1936
20 Mells deeds
21 SMA, minute 15 January 1943
22 Lord Hylton, *History of Kilmersdon* (1910)
23 *Somerset Guardian,* 30 March 1895
24 SMA, misc corr
25 Ibid
26 Ibid
27 Ibid
28 Ibid
29 SMA, minute 10 September 1921
30 SMA, minute 23 March 1923
31 SMA, misc corr
32 *Western Daily Press,* 6 August 1927
33 SMA, misc corr
34 Bulley (1952), 69
35 NCB records, Vobster plans and sections
36 Beech, *Mining Progress through the Ages*
37 Paulton Foundry ledger
38 Paulton Foundry ledger
39 Catalogue of Abandoned Mines of Somerset
40 SRO, DD/WG 35
41 HM Inspector of Mines, report (1887)
42 Paulton Foundry ledger

43 SRO, DD/WG 35
44 SMA, misc corr
45 DofC, Nettlebridge papers
46 NCB records, section of 1825
47 DofC, Nettlebridge papers
48 Ibid
49 Bulley (1953), 24
50 DofC, Nettlebridge papers
51 Radstock notebooks
52 DofC, Nettlebridge papers
53 Information on Sweetleaze and Strap from Radstock notebooks
54 SRO, DD/WG 35
55 HLRO, minutes of evidence on S & D Bill, Vol 44 Grp 1 (1871), evidence of Joseph Hill and William Evans
56 SRO, DD/WG 33, evidence of John Batey on S & D Amalgamation Bill (1876)
57 SMA, minute 26 March 1926
58 SMA, minute 13 May 1932
59 Beauchamp records
60 Report to Lord Hylton (1939)
61 All lease information on New Rock from Beauchamp records, New Rock deeds
62 Beauchamp records, output statistics
63 SMA, misc corr
64 History of this development from NCB records

APPENDIX

List of Shaft Diameters and Depths

Colliery	Shaft diameter ft in	Maximum shaft depth (ft)
Amesbury	?	200
Barlake	5 0	435
Bilboa	?	240
Bishop Sutton (Old)	?	304
Bishop Sutton (New)	9 0	877
Braysdown	10 0	1,834
Breach (Vobster)	?	867
Brewer's	?	102
Brombel	4 6	?
Bromley	4 6	475
Burchells	?	148
Camerton (Old)	7 0	921
Camerton (New)	8 0	1,818
Clandown	6 0	1,437
Conygre (Upper)	8 0	1,038
Conygre (Lower)	8 0	1,128
Crossways	5 0	144
Downside, *see* Strap		
Dunkerton	10 0	1,651
Edford	6 0	798
Farmborough	?	1,413
Farrington	9 0	588
Foxcote	9 0	1,416
Frys Bottom	9 0	588
Greyfield	10 0	900
Hayeswood	6 0	642
Huish	8 0	570
Kilmersdon	10 6	1,582
Littlebrook	5ft x 5ft	215
Luckington	6 0	135
Ludlows	8 0	1,686
Mackintosh	8 3	1,620
Mearns	4 6	279
Mells	9 0	540
Mendip, *see* Strap		

Middle Pit	10	0	1,791
Mooresland	5	0	231
Moorewood (Old)	4	6	365
Moorewood (New)	9	0	888
Nettlebridge	6	0	705
Newbury (Old)	?		250
Newbury	9	0	720
New Rock	4	6	1,182
Norton Hill (Old)	4	6	1,247
Norton Hill (New)	13	6	1,503
Old Grove	4	6	1,373
Old Mills	11	0	1,098
Old Pit	6	0	942
Old Rock	4	6	711
Old Welton	4	6	1,646
Paulton Bottom	4	6	60
Paulton Engine	9	0	609
Paulton Ham	6	0	552
Paulton Hill	?		798
Pensford	14	0	1,494
Pitcot	5	0	555
Priston	8	0	750
Radford	6	0	1,152
Ringing	?		360
Rydon's	?		312
Salisbury	6	0	150
Shoscombe	10ft x 7ft		360
Simons Hill	4	6	672
Smallcombe	7	0	1,074
Springfield	9	6	965
Strap	10	6	1,838
Tyning New (Timsbury)	4	6	630
Tyning (Radstock)	8	0	1,007
Vobster	10	0	990
Wellsway	4	6	754
Welton Hill	6	0	603
Withy Mills	4	6	804
Woodborough	5	3	426
Writhlington (Lower)	10	0	1,461
Writhlington (Upper)	11	3	942

ACKNOWLEDGEMENTS

Possibly the most sustaining feature of this work has been the enthusiasm for the project shown by those to whom we have turned for help. Undoubtedly the first word of thanks must go to the secretary and staff of the National Coal Board at Kilmersdon Colliery, without whose initial and subsequent help this book could never have been written. We wish also to express our gratitude to the following for their assistance: Bath & Camerton Archaeological Society; Bath Reference Library; the late G. E. L. B. Beauchamp; Board of Trade; Bristol City Museum & Art Gallery; Bristol Public Library; University of Bristol, Wills Memorial Library; British Railways; Duchy of Cornwall; the late Edric Hodder; Haldane & McLaren, W.S.; House of Lords Record Office; Mrs E. Howell; Lord Hylton of Ammerdown; W. Vaughan-Jenkins; W. Rees-Mogg; Miss J. Saunders; the *Somerset Guardian*; Somerset Record Office.

There remain to be mentioned those who have helped us during three years of field work. We have spoken to over 300 people—miners, retired miners, and others—who have provided us with the facts and details about 'their' collieries, the *minutiae* of everyday mining life. It is impossible to acknowledge each individual—indeed, there are many whose names we never knew—but each has willingly taken time to answer our many questions, referred us to workmates for further information, demonstrated features 'on site', and, last but not least, refreshed us in our enquiries with food and drink. The help of the people of North Somerset has been indispensable and to them we offer our sincere thanks.

The final word must go to our wives, for their patience during what has been, for us all at times, a full-time occupation.

INDEXES

Figures in **bold** type indicate page numbers for plates in text

GENERAL

Absenteeism, 36
Accidents, 44, 66, 77, 89, 94, 96, 99, 102, 173, 176, 178, 179, 202, 219, 229, 234, 246 (*see also* Explosions *and* Flooding)
Acts of Parliament:
Coal Act, 1938, 25
Coal Mines Act, 1930, 25
Coal Mines Act, 1954, 256
Dorset & Somerset Canal Act, 1795, 18
Mines Minimum Wage Act, 1912, 32
Mining Industry Act, 1926, 214
Somersetshire Coal Canal Act, 1794, 183
Adams family, coal owners, 35, 92, 97, 99, 105
Adits, *see* Drifts
Aerial ropeways, 127, 158, 254
Anstie, J., geologist, 18, 240, 245
Ashman, William, engineer, 91
Avonmouth Coalfield, 28, 30

Batey, J., mining engineer, 57, 111, 159, 194, 234, 248
Baths, *see* Pithead baths
Beam engines:
Cornish type, 34, **51**, 57, 76, **155**, 157, 164, 181, 194, 198, 199, 209, 216, 236
Newcomen type, 89, 92, 94
Beauchamp family, coalowners:
Louis, 133, 212-13, 214, 215, 216, 249, 254
Sir Frank, 22, 25, 26, 113, 117, 124, 125, 128, 129, 130, 133,
135, 136, 150, 152, 159, 163, 171, 173, 180, 193, 202, 212-13, 214, 215, 216, 236, 249
William, 133, 147, 148, 159, 162, 212-13, 239
Beaumont Kennedy & Co, 105
Bird, F. J., colliery owner, 148, 151, 152, 159
Bishop Sutton Coal Co, 57
Bishop Sutton Colliery Co, 57
Bishop Sutton Colliery Co Ltd, 57, 58
Blagdon Light Railway, 18, 58-9
Boreholes, 28, 69, 126, 144, 255
Braysdown Colliery Co, 201
Brickworks, 71, 77, 81, 127, 148, 150, 182, 206
Bristol & North Somerset Railway, 18, 71, 77, 133, 134, 139, 143, 148, 157, 186
Bristol City Docks, 19
Bristol Coalfield, 24, 28, 32
Bromley Colliery Co, 59
Bush family, coalowners, 94, 99, 146, 180

Cages:
general, 45, 47, 66, 76, 107, 111, 127, 167, 171, 176, 179, 197, 199, 201, 211, 219, 238, 240, 254, 256-7, 258
introduction of, 44, 45
Charmborough Collieries Ltd, 27, 250
Clandown Colliery Co, 151
Clutton Coal Co, 78
Coal Commission, 25

MINES